D1097906

COWBOY ARITHMETIC

COWBOY ARITHMETIC

"Cattle as an Investment"

by

HAROLD L. OPPENHEIMER

THE INTERSTATE
Printers & Publishers, Inc.
Danville, Illinois

Library of Congress
Catalog Card Number 61-12775

Printed and Published by
THE INTERSTATE
Printers & Publishers, Inc.
Danville, Illinois

First Printing, September, 1961
Second Printing, November, 1961

PRINTED IN U. S. A.

PREFACE

The material in this book was generally prepared during the period 1955-1960, which has been a time of great fluctuation in cattle market prices, weather conditions, and various governmental actions.

Wherever possible, particularly in the case of financial projections, an attempt was made to date the price level used. However, the different periods of the writing will account for some of the apparent discrepancies.

During the five year period between 1955 and 1960 and even up to the present date, the cattle prices have fluctuated within the range of the post World War II high which occurred in 1951 and the low which occurred in 1953.

In this general connection, it should also be remembered that various governmental programs change radically from year to year and that some of the discrepancies on this point within the book are also due to the time at which the chapter was written.

Sincerely yours,
H. L. Oppenheimer

TABLE OF CONTENTS

Part I—OPERATIONS

Part II—HISTORY AND THE GOVERNMENT

Part III—ECONOMICS

PART I

OPERATIONS

Chapter I

Introduction

Between the gleam in a bull's eye as he chases a heifer across a meadow and a cut of prime steak at the Waldorf-Astoria is a vast and complicated business.

It is unique in many respects:

1. The fact that over 20,000,000 Americans are directly or indirectly employed may make it the largest business in the United States.
2. Over 40% of the surface area of the United States is being used in it.
3. In an average year it is the chief source of income for eleven states.
4. In dividing the business up into its almost unrelated segments one finds that some sections are the last word in modern industrial techniques and some haven't changed since the days of Matt Dillon.
5. In some phases it is the most unionized and government controlled business in the country; in other phases it may be the last stronghold of a frontier type of American rugged individualism.

What are these businesses that make up this industry? What is a typical sequence of events that ends up with steak on a New York restaurant table?

On a northern New Mexico ranch where it takes 40 acres to support a cow all year round, a Hereford bull bred twenty cows during the period of June to September in 1957.

Nine months later in April of 1958 one of the cows gave birth to a 90 pound bull calf. In the June roundup of that year the calf was castrated, branded with the owner's brand, dehorned, and vaccinated. During the six months of the summer and early fall while he was nursing his mother and also eating a little bit of grass he rapidly put on weight. On the fall roundup in November he was weaned at a weight of 400 pounds and put in another pasture with calves of his own age and weight.

During the winter he was fed cottonseed cake, a small amount of grain, and when a rare snow covered the winter grass, the rancher gave him some hay. In April of 1959 he is a full year old and weighs 550 pounds. He came through the winter thin but healthy. The 150 pound gain went into bone and frame and not into flesh.

The rancher has made a practice of leasing pastures every year to the north in the famous Kansas blue stem where the great buffalo herds used to concentrate. The yearling is now shipped there along with his companions. During the Kansas summer he now puts on 250 pounds of gain. He has done a lot more growing and has put on a certain amount of "grass flesh." The high protein of the Kansas blue stem puts on a little firmer flesh than most grasses; this is known as a "hard finish."

As an 800 pound "late yearling steer" he is now shipped to the stockyards in Kansas City. Here he and his group are purchased by a large Iowa grain farmer who runs his own feed lot to consume the portion of his crop that he doesn't put under government loan. The Iowa feeder puts him on a mixed ration of corn and hay for about thirty days gradually increasing the proportion of corn. At the end of ninety days he is given all of the grain he can eat. He is kept on this program for another ninety days. During this period he has been putting on an average of 2½ pounds per day. He gained more at the beginning but the weight that he put on at the end was the weight and "finish" which pushed him up from a classification of "high choice" to "prime."

From the Iowa farm he is sent to the Chicago Stockyards as a 1,200 pound prime two-year-old steer. Here he is bought by one of the major packing companies. A federal agent marks his carcass as prime after he is slaughtered. With the head, hide, legs, etc. off, his carcass "dresses out" at 800 pounds. The packing house sells him to one of the major New York wholesalers and he is shipped east by refrigerator car. The wholesaler sends the cheaper cuts to the grocery stores and butcher shops; the best cuts go to the restaurants and land on some employer's expense account.

The entire cycle from conception to the table took approximately three years. The animal or his carcass was physically moved eight times. Ownership changed hands five times. It could have been seven if he were handled by traders at the two stockyards in addition to commission men. Stockyard "traders" buy cattle for their own account for resale. "Commission men" are merely brokers and title doesn't change.

This book is going to deal with a specialized phase of the industry—the commercial beef breeding herd. We start with the bred cow and we stop when the offspring is a year old and is on the way to a feed lot.

When we say a "commercial" breeding herd, we are differentiating from the registered pedigreed breeding herd which we will cover more thoroughly in a later chapter. Registered herds are those whose members are eligible for pedigree papers with one of the large purebred associations. The principal beef breeds in the United States with large associations are Herefords, Angus, Shorthorn, Brangus, and Santa Gertrudis. There are various qualifications to register an animal with these associations but in general they require precise identification of the dam and sire who either themselves are listed with the association or who have accepted lineage such as registration with the British Hereford Association (English Hereford Book).

Most good commercial breeding herds consist of uniform members of one of the principal breeds but, because groups of bulls are run together for operating economics, the progeny are not eligible for registration as the individual sire cannot be identified. These animals are "purebred" but not "registered."

It is common in most of the commercial breeding herds to bring in from the outside, registered pedigreed bulls of a quality superior to the general level of the herd at three year intervals. This has two advantages:

1. The bull might be able to sire as many as thirty calves so the additional investment in a superior animal will help raise the quality of a considerable portion of the commercial breeding herd.
2. The average commercial breeder does not want to use his own bulls for a long period as some of them would undoubtedly be breeding back their own daughters or mothers and an infusion of new blood is considered a good practice.

Furthermore, registered herds are handled more economically in small farm areas where there is adequate fencing and cross pastures. There are large commercial breeders who run a separated registered herd as a side line but this is an unusual practice.

In the coming chapter on registered herds there will be a further discussion of the comparative qualities of different breeds and a brief resumé of their history in the United States.

Returning to our primary subject, most large commercial breeding herds in the United States are located in an area running from the immediate west slope of the Rockies to a line formed by a North-South extension of the Missouri-Kansas border. The only major exception to this is the recent advent of the state of Florida upon the scene.

Generally, the large scale presence of commercial breeding herds is found where there is grass and rough forage but where the land is not suitable for grain or cotton cultivation and beyond a minimum of 50 miles distance from any major city. In areas suitable for grain cultivation, it is generally more economical to run feeder operations than breeding herds. Near a large city the dairy farmer can afford to bid more for pasture and feed than the beef rancher which makes the latter's costs prohibitive and he must move beyond the radius of economical milk delivery.

Chapter II

General Facts on Cattle Breeding

1. The four largest breeds of beef cattle in the U. S. are Herefords, Angus, Polled Herefords, and Shorthorns. The Herefords are reddish brown and white with white faces and horns. The Angus are black without horns. The Polled Herefords are Herefords without horns. The Shorthorns are varying colors, predominantly roan, with horns.

2. Through the South and Southwest the primary breeds have been crossed with the Indian Brahman strain because of its greater adaptability to the heat and have formed stabilized cross breeds such as the Santa Gertrudis, Braefords, Brangus, etc.

3. The period of gestation of a cow from breeding to birth is slightly over nine (9) months.

4. A calf is normally weaned at seven (7) months, but can be given supplementary feed from about two (2) months with an earlier weaning period. "Creep feeding" is a means of feeding calves grain while they are nursing by means of some mechanical device that the cows can't get to.

5. On a small farm, a mature bull can service 30 to 35 cows. On a rough western range you might need 1 bull to 15 cows.

6. To be eligible for registration in the Hereford Association, the calf must be out of a cow that was not under fifteen (15) months old when bred and sired by a bull not under twelve (12) months old at the time of breeding.

7. Good breeding practices customarily add about four (4) months to the minimum ages. In the case of females on the open ranges where they will have to calve without supervision, it is customary to breed at two years, to drop at two years nine months.

8. There is some variation around the country, but the following terminology is used in the state of Missouri. A young animal is called a "calf" for the first year, after which it is called a "yearling." A female is a "heifer calf"; a male is a "bull calf" until it is castrated, after which it is called a "steer calf." Animals slightly over a year old are called "long yearlings"; under a year, "short yearlings." Up to two

years a female is called a "heifer." After she has had a calf, she is called a "first calf heifer." After the first calf is weaned she is a full fledged "cow."

9. The following weight schedules are normal for animals in good healthy condition, but not fattened for market, plus or minus 20%: New born calf–90 lb. Weaned six (6) month calf–400 lb. Yearling–650 lb. Eighteen (18) month heifer–800 lb. 2 year old cow–950 lb. 3 year old cow–1,050 lb. 5 year old cow–1,100 lb. 4 year old bull–1,500 lb. In the case of animals fattened for the show ring to create a better appearance, you can add 300 lb. to the preceding figures. This latter weight in no way improves their breeding qualities. In fact you have to go to a lot of trouble to take them off feed slowly before you put them on the farm or ranch.

10. Cows normally come in heat about every twenty-one (21) days for a period of about 12 to 18 hours. Successful breeding must take place during that short period of time. Artificial insemination is common for dairy animals but rare for beef herds. Hand breeding is used only for registered show animals and practically never for grade breeding herds.

11. Calf crop percentage refers to the number of calves successfully weaned out of a given number of cows. This is the pay-off on a cattle breeding operation and is the best criterion of the efficiency of the operation. The national average runs around 70%. A good operation would hit 80%. An outstanding operation would be 90%. A small herd on a small farm can normally do 10% better than an open range operation.

12. Factors affecting calf percentage are:

a. Age and condition of the cows.

b. Age and condition of the bulls.

c. Number of bulls to cows.

d. Area over which bulls must travel to find cows.

e. Supervision of herd during breeding. On one of our range operations, a full time man does nothing else for two months but rides herd to see that the bulls get to any cow that appears to be in heat.

f. Supervision of cows during calving. It doesn't do any good to get the calf on the ground and have it die the first week. In the case of first calf heifers, inadequate supervision may cause the loss of both the cow and the calf during birthing.

g. Timing of breeding. In the northern areas it is important to see that the calves drop after the risks of blizzard are over.

Calves are generally weaned between six and eight months. (Courtesy, American Hereford Assn.)

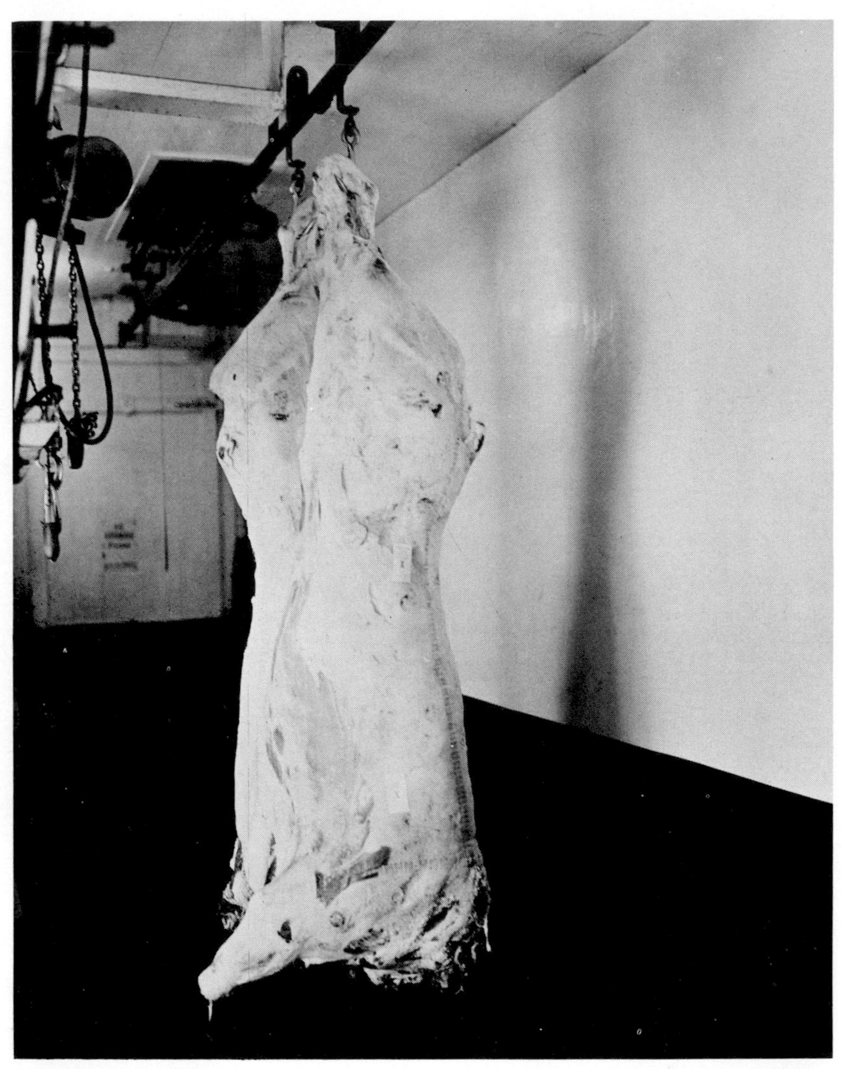

A dressed-out beef generally weighs between 55% and 65% of its live weight. (Courtesy, American Hereford Assn.)

13. Good uniform breeding herds are never found in the big public meat markets except in times of disaster. It is important to assemble breeding herds directly from the farms or ranches as they are exposed to all kinds of diseases down at the stockyards. Generally, animals at the stockyards go directly to the packers or to feed lots and rarely to breeding herds. Good uniform animals of a single brand out of a herd that has been properly culled and which have been bred to known bulls of good quality are worth about 3c per pound more than identical appearing animals at the stockyards where no history is known.

14. On February 1, 1960 the approximate prices of the weights and classes of animals listed in paragraph "9" of this section were as follows at the Kansas City Stockyards:

400 lb. heifer calves	$110.00
650 lb. yearling heifers	170.00
1,050 lb. 3 year old cows	210.00

In buying the same class of animals in assembled herds off the ranch, you would be easily justified in going $10.00 to $15.00 higher.

15. The normal mortality on a breeding herd runs about 3% a year on older animals and about 4% on calves. If you don't have any epidemics or particular catastrophes, you can cut the figure in half. A blizzard could cause a 20% loss in a herd of young calves. In the 1948 blizzards through Nebraska and the Dakotas, herd losses averaged around 15% to 25%. On a small farm operation, mortality figures will be half those on a large ranch.

Chapter III

Pasture and Feed

Considering the fact that there are over 20,000 volumes on this subject in the Library of Congress and that every major university has departments of men who have devoted their entire lives to the subject, it is rather presumptuous to attempt to cover it in a chapter of 18 pages. At the risk of boring experienced cattlemen, we are going to assume that the reader's sole background in agriculture has been keeping dandelions and crab grass out of his front lawn.

At the moment of consumption, the menu of cattle can be divided into these six general categories:

1. Pasture
2. Hay
3. Silage
4. Grain
5. Concentrates
6. Salt, minerals, and vitamins

The type, quantity, or combination of these elements of feed is governed by the following factors:

1. In what part of the country are you?
2. What is the season of the year?
3. With what class of cattle are you dealing? Nursing cows? Yearling steers? Newly weaned calves?
4. What are you trying to accomplish? Maintain dry cows in normal healthy shape? Fatten two-year-old steers for a market 90-days hence, etc.?
5. What is the cheapest combination that can be fed that will best accomplish your mission in your particular area during the particular season in which you are working?

In order to review some of the terminology used, let us take the life cycle of oats as commonly used in the state of Missouri.

In the month of March or earlier the field is "plowed," which consists of turning the soil to a depth of somewhere between four and nine inches. After this, the heavy clods of turned earth are "disked."

This consists of running over them with multiple blades of circular steel, which breaks the clods up into small increments. Occasionally, but not commonly, the field might be "harrowed." The harrow is a series of spikes, towed behind a tractor or team of horses, which breaks up the soil into even smaller increments. The grain is then put in by a "drill." A drill consists of a grain box in which the oats are stored plus a series of disks with a means of letting the seed come out of the grain box in the proper proportions so as to feed a constant amount per acre on the field. Behind the disks and the dropping grain is often a series of small chains which drag over the ground behind the seed to help cover it up. Drills can be regulated so as to put more or less seed in the ground, and the height can be regulated so as to bury the seed anywhere from a quarter of an inch under the surface to as much as two inches. Many drills are so arranged that varieties of seed can be planted at the same time and at different levels.

Very often oats is used as a "nurse crop" which means that a more delicate seed is planted at the same time. The oats will grow faster and hold the soil to protect the other seed from too much sun or washing away while it is taking hold. The other plant grows up among the oats and after the oats crop is removed, the other type of seed will take over the pasture.

Approximately thirty to sixty days after the oats have been planted the leaf-blades of the plant will be up somewhere between four and eight inches. At this time, if the ground is frozen or hard enough that the hoofs of cattle will not chop up the field too much, the oats "grass" can be grazed by cattle as a pasture.

By May the oats plant is in the "milk" stage. This means that if you take one of the seeds in the newly formed "head" and squeeze it with your thumbnail, it is soft and a milky-like substance will come out. At this time the entire plant can be cut off at ground level and made into "hay."

The process of putting up hay is as follows: First, the field is mowed, which is the process of cutting off the plant; then, it is raked into "windrows." These are long rows of piled up plants which are allowed to cure and dry out in the sun for a few days. In the event that a rain should come during this period, it is necessary to delay baling until the plant dries out again. Rain in moderate amounts on the plant while it is in the windrow is not damaging to its eventual use as hay.

The next process involves baling the windrow. A baler gathers the hay, compresses it, packs it into squares which it automatically ties with wire or twine and ejects onto the field. This is a square baler.

Recently round balers have come into use which roll the hay into cylindrical bales and wrap them with twine. Round bales are used principally in the more arid or northern areas where they can be left lying on the field and used for winter pastures, where the cattle will be subsequently turned in on them and where they will be eaten on the spot.

After the oats hay has been baled, it is picked up from the field sometimes by automatic equipment but mostly by hand and either transported to a barn or neatly stacked and covered.

In some sections of the country, the old-fashioned stack of loose hay is still used rather than the bales. To feed, a wagon is moved next to the stack and the farmer loads the wagon from the stack with a pitchfork. Nowadays, this is extremely rare. In some modern operations a stack is still used, but the entire stack itself is winched on to a sledge and towed to the cattle. In either bales or stacks, there is some spoilage and wastage on the outside layers which are actually exposed to the weather. There is more spoilage in damp, wet climates than there is in colder, dryer climates.

In all cases of hay usage, the rancher should calculate the loss in hay from use in the open as compared to the amount of labor that is saved in having to move the hay, stack it and put it in the barn, then rehaul it out to the cattle in the winter time in daily increments. Very often the less desirable and least expensive hay is left in the open, while choice alfalfa is stacked in the barn. Each rancher makes his own compromise between the various cost factors involved.

Let us return back to our oats field. The farmer had several other alternatives to making hay out of his oats field. He could have let the plant continue to mature until June or July. At that time the grain would have become dry and hard and he could have gone over the field with a "combine." A combine cuts off the top part of the plant containing the grain head; separates the non-usable "chaff" from the grain pellet; expels the chaff; and retains the grain.

After the combine has removed the grain from the now yellow and dried up plant, what is left in the field is "oats straw." The oats straw could now be cut from the field, raked, and baled. Generally, the food value and other uses of oats straw is so little that, except in times of drought, it does not pay financially to do this.

The oats straw field, however, could very well be used for cattle grazing in the late summer or fall as it would furnish roughage if nothing else. Very commonly another plant which matures later is put in at the same time as the oats and the combination of the oats straw and the second plant could very well offer excellent early fall pasture.

While not too common with oats, the farmer had another alternative back at the time the plant was in the "milk" stage. At this time he could have cut off the entire plant while it was green and had it chopped into small particles and fed it to cattle in a feed lot as "green chop." Also, at this time, he could have taken his "green chop" and put it in a "silo."

This could have been a cylindrical upright type made of concrete or a deep trench in the ground. When the chopped up "silage" was put away, it should have been heavily watered and packed down tightly so that as little air as possible could get into the bottom layers. When this is done, after a period of time, a fermentation process takes place, which preserves the silage from spoilage as long as it can be kept from the air. Normally, in a silo the outer one-fifth will spoil, but this will form a seal and the inner part can be preserved for as long as four or five years. There is some loss in feed value every year, but properly put up silage can go for a long period of time.

In summary, from the oats plant you can get green pasture; oats hay; grain; chaff; straw; straw pasture; green chop; and silage.

Before continuing, it might be well to review changes in names on another principal feed crop–corn. The plant that is left after the grain has been harvested is called a stalk, and stalk fields are excellent early winter pastures when other supplement is given along with the field. Most automatic pickers leave one or two bushels in the field which the cattle can pick up but which are not valuable enough to justify retrieving for resale. In the case of corn, the dried stalk when put up as feed is called "corn stover." Corn silage, which involves chopping up grain, stalk and all while it is still in the unripened stage, is one of the principal feeds through much of the Middlewest.

In good fertile bottom land, eighteen tons per acre of silage would not be out of line for either a corn or milo field. Where good soil and modern equipment are available there is probably no way the same amount of land could produce any more feed.

In many parts of the country, the field containing the straw or stalk that is left after the grain has been removed is called a "stubble field." Generally, there are areas of such fields near the corners or in ditches where it was uneconomical for the farmer to attempt to cultivate. Consequently, most such fields have small portions of native grass that can be eaten along with the stubble. The combination very often makes excellent grazing during the months of October and November.

1. PASTURES

Pastures fall into three general categories—native, improved, and special situations.

Native grass pastures, as here used, mean not only the natural grasses that existed prior to the white man but also the developed grasses that have been introduced over the last hundred years, which spread of their own accord, and which do not normally require any work on the part of the landowner other than controlling brush, occasionally adding fertilizer, and possibly mowing weeds. Blue stem, blue grass, grama, Johnson, various native clovers, Bermuda, St. Augustine, and buffalo all fall into this category. In addition to the "native grasses" there are many natural bushes or other plants such as sage, piñon, some forms of cactus and others which offer forage to livestock at various times of the year.

By "improved" pasture we refer to good tillable land that is seeded with developed hybrid or imported grasses and given constant care in the way of fertilizer, mowing, periodic reseeding, etc. Commonly used grasses are brome, fescue, orchard, blue grass, Bermuda, canary grass, St. Augustine and bird's foot trefoil. With these grasses, or used separately, are some of the legumes such as alfalfa, red clover, alsike clover, and Korean lespedeza. These grasses and legumes mature at different times of the year and some could hit the height of their growth while others are in decline. Consequently, it is customary to sow a mixture. Often a small amount of the native grasses are sown at the same time to give a broader spread.

For the purposes of this book, the chief distinction between native and improved pastures is that the native pastures are on marginal-type soil or terrain while the improved pastures are on highly desirable land suitable for cultivation. Consequently, in the latter case the growth qualities and the desirability of the land are such that every seven or eight years, it would probably pay to plow up the pasture and reseed it with an appropriate new mixture. Very often on an improved pasture that is untenanted for a number of years, there is a gradual increase in weed growth, a decrease in productivity through lack of fertilizer, and the running over of the pasture by hardier native semi-weed grasses of small nutritional value or of a shorter season such as cheat or foxtail.

In some areas of the country the most desirable feature of a grass is its ability to "cure" at the end of the summer and serve as a winter grazing feed. In northern arid states such as Wyoming, Montana, Nebraska or South Dakota, this is the principal winter feed with hay being used only during the periods that the ground is covered with snow.

Under "other situations" we want to list: (1) the short-term grazing of stubble fields mentioned before, (2) the early spring or late fall grazing of green crop fields, (3) the planting of short-term, one-shot forage crops such as sudan. In the areas of Kansas, Oklahoma, Northern Texas and Eastern Colorado, the grazing of winter wheat is a major phase of the cattle economy.

In this particular area, the ground is dry enough that by having cattle graze the young wheat as it is started helps to pack the plant in the ground and causes the wheat to better stool out. Also in this area, the cattle grazing not only does not damage the future grain crop, but in most cases it helps to increase the net yield.

There are a few disadvantages to wheat grazing. First, the value of the eventual grain crop is so much more to the wheat farmer than the rents he can get for grazing that he usually puts in the grazing contract the requirement that the cattle owner must move his cattle on forty-eight hours notice. This is done so that on warm, wet days, later in the season, when the cattle's hooves sinking into the soil can seriously damage the crop, the farmer has the right to force the rancher to move them. Likewise, as soon as the wheat stem is high enough to start forming a "joint," it is necessary that the cattle be moved off as any further grazing from that period on will stop the development of the grain head.

Winter rye has approximately the same feed value as wheat and the same season but it produces substantially more grazing. Where there is no particular desire to get a grain crop and the grazing is the most important factor, then rye makes a better deal than wheat.

Sudan is a tropical grass that has to be replanted each year, which can be seeded in April and which will produce a tremendous amount of growth on a very small acreage during the months of July and August. This is the usual season when all other pasture grasses are somewhat dormant and helps hold the fort until the rest of them begin growing again in September.

Lespedeza, a legume, has somewhat the same season as sudan, hitting its main growth in August. In the case of sudan there are certain seasons and periods when the plant develops a prussic acid content that can poison the cattle. This is commonly found in the first new second growth after a hay crop has been taken or a new growth after a period of prolonged drought.

In the case of alfalfa or clover pasture, when there is not an appreciable amount of other grasses mixed in with them, there is a hazard of "bloat" in the early spring, after a heavy rain, and for a couple of weeks after the first frost. Pasturing new alfalfa fields is an extremely tricky business and the cattle should be looked at a minimum of three times a day. On the first indication of any animal suffering from bloat, the entire herd should be moved immediately. In the late summer after a one-month dry period or several weeks after the first frost in the fall when the leaves have begun to turn brown and dry, it is reasonably safe. While this is not 100% accurate, the danger is somewhat less if the cattle simultaneously have free access to other grasses at the same time as the alfalfa field. A mixture of other grasses and feed with the alfalfa helps to prevent bloat, and also there seems to be a tendency for cattle to avoid the alfalfa during the dangerous time if there are plenty of other palatable feeds available.

2. HAY

Hay can be put up from almost any edible pasture grass or plant. The time of the year in which it is put up can affect the feed value as much as plus or minus 50%. As in all other feeds, the principal nutritional elements are proteins, carbohydrates, minerals and vitamins. The non-nutritional roughage element, however, is necessary as it is needed in the digestive process. However, because the labor, machinery and storage costs of putting it up, transporting it, and feeding it out represent over 70% of its cost, it is uneconomical to handle anything but a high feed value hay.

With the sudden increase in labor and machinery over the last ten years, the trend seems to be more and more to alfalfa and away from the less nutritional grass hays. The mathematics are simple. Let us compare alfalfa, timothy, and prairie hay:[1]

	% Protein	*% Digestible*	*% Total Digestible Nutrients*	*% Calcium*	*Carotene (mg./lb.)*
Alfalfa	15.3	10.9	50.7	1.47	8.2
Timothy	6.6	3.0	49.1	.35	4.4
Prairie Hay	4.4	.9	45.7	.88	3.6

On an overall dollar valuation, a ton of alfalfa could conservatively be said to be worth 40% more as a feed than the other two on the protein element alone.

Let us consider the following costs as a constant for all three kinds of hay in Western Kansas in 1959:

[1]*Beef Cattle,* Snapp and Neumann, 5th edition, John Wiley and Sons, Inc., New York, 1960, Appendix, Table 1, p. 652.

$8/ton to mow, rake, and bale it.
$3/ton to load it in a truck.
$3/ton to haul it to the point of storage.
$4/ton to feed it out in increments over the winter.

$18/ton total in labor and machinery to put it up and feed it out.

Now let us assume that timothy and prairie hay cost $4/ton in rent and growing costs on the field but that alfalfa costs $1 more for a total of $5/ton. That puts final "to be fed" cost of alfalfa at $23 and the other two at $22. However, if alfalfa is 40% more valuable, there is a profit of $8/ton at consumption over the other two.

The most critical thing to remember is not to permit a baling crew to put up the bales if the hay is wet or if it is about to rain. Hay left in the windrows will dry out, but once it is in the bale it will spoil. Wet hay also generates heat during the spoilage process and there has been many a barn that has burned due to heat generated by wet hay.

Older cows will eat hay with a certain amount of spoilage; calves generally will not.

Straight alfalfa normally does not do well in the process of round bales which are left on the ground for winter feed. The principle of the round bale is that it will shed water and does not have to be removed from the field, saving the labor cost of hauling it and the labor cost of bringing it out again in the winter. This works satisfactorily with grass hay which has long stems that hold the round bales together and help shed the water. In the case of alfalfa or most legume hays, the water isn't shed as well and the bales break apart too easily in the winter with the result that there is an unnecessary amount of wastage.

Part of the principle of the round bale is that it is difficult for the cattle to break it open, so that when once a bale is broken open, a number of animals come around and eat it before moving on to the next bale. With legume hay round bales, this does not work out as well and cattle may break open a considerable number attempting to get at the choice hay in the middle, leaving the slightly less palatable outside hay to lie on the ground and be wasted.

The round bale left on the ground also works better in a dry climate. In the more humid climates the twine tends to rot and a good number of the bales will fall open and partially disintegrate. Likewise, in dry climates the spoilage on the outside from rainfall is generally less than two inches thick, while in areas of great rainfall it might penetrate the bale to as much as four inches.

Consider the fact that there is a labor and equipment charge of

$3/ton to move the bale from the field to a stack and a cost of $4/ton to haul it out in increments during the winter with a total charge of $7/ton. On prairie hay selling for $22/ton, this represents about one-third of the cost of the hay. Consequently, the round bales left on the ground could spoil and be wasted to a 30% extent and the rancher is still ahead of the game.

In the State of Missouri during the early part of the summer, alfalfa will shrink 10% in weight within 72 hours from the time that it is cut and baled. Therefore, if you are hiring custom work done, it is a matter of considerable advantage if you negotiate your contracts so that the weighing be accomplished several days after it is first cut. Buying hay in a dry barn that has been stored for four or five months and has probably shrunk 20% by evaporation of moisture justifies a considerably higher price per ton than the same hay would have brought on the day it was mowed.

Alfalfa suffers a fair amount of deterioration in feed value carried over from one year to another. The carotene content goes down rapidly in the very beginning and the protein content deteriorates somewhat but in a much more gradual manner. On the other hand, the moisture content is also going down and acts as a somewhat compensating cost factor if the price of the hay is being calculated on a tonnage basis.

Using alfalfa as an example, here are a number of points to be remembered:

1. There are over twenty common varieties of alfalfa and in seeding a field it is well worth while to pick the type best suited to the climate and soil condition of your ranch.
2. On good nonirrigated bottom land along the Missouri River, an alfalfa field should produce four cuttings a season, averaging out one ton to the acre per cutting, giving a total production for the year of four tons.
3. In irrigated land in Southern Wyoming, an alfalfa field should produce two cuttings in a season for a total of two tons to the acre.
4. In the Missouri example your first cutting generally has a lot of weed growth in it and is substantially coarser. That is why "first cutting alfalfa" usually sells for about 20% less per ton than the later cuttings.
5. In some more Northern areas, it is customary not to remove the last cutting from the field but to lightly graze it and let the balance remain as some winter protection for the plant so as to get an earlier and heavier first cutting the following year.

6. The more leafy the hay is with less stem and less extraneous weed matter, the higher the "grade" is. Cutting the alfalfa when it is in partial bloom gives it a substantially higher protein value than cutting it after the "bloom."

7. Alfalfa generally gets its best growth after the second year from the time of planting and gradually begins to deteriorate until the sixth year when it generally pays to plow up the field and replant it.

8. Alfalfa is a leguminous plant similar to the clovers and helps replenish the nitrogen in the soil that might have been depleted by previous grain crops.

9. In the State of Missouri in the year 1960 it cost approximately $30.00 per acre to prepare the soil, fertilize and plant alfalfa.

10. It cost $9.00 per ton to have the hay mowed, raked, and baled, with an extra $3.00 per ton if it was picked up off the field and trucked to a nearby barn or stack.

11. In the month of February 1960 in Western Missouri, No. 1 leafy alfalfa was bringing $25.00 per ton.

12. Unless extremely reliable custom workers are involved, it is always better to have everything done on hay calculated at a per ton price rather than at a per bale price, even if a premium has to be paid.

The average bale should weigh between 65 and 75 pounds. However, if a baling crew is being paid on a per bale basis, it is to the crew's own self interest to make the bales as light as possible and 40-pound bales might be the result, which would double your cost per ton.

3. SILAGE

Silage can be made from almost any edible plant. As far as the United States is concerned, corn silage and sorghum silage are by far the most common. In all uses of silage, it is essential that the plant be cut while it is green, that an adequate amount of water be put with it when it is put in the silo, and that it be thoroughly packed down so as to allow as little air as possible to reach it. Let us review corn silage as an example:

1. It generally has about half the feed value of alfalfa hay. Consequently, with the constant labor and machinery cost of feeding, there would be some uneconomic elements. However, it does lend itself to the latest mechanical equipment for feeding in troughs, and if this equipment were available, the labor could even be less than the handling of hay bales.

2. Eighteen tons of production from an acre on good land in a year would not be unusual.
3. A principal element of corn silage is the amount of actual corn grain left in the silage. Obviously, silage made from a field that was producing 10 bushels of corn to the acre would be worth substantially less than silage from a field that was producing 40 bushels to the acre.
4. The amount of value and percentage of corn in the silage can be approximately determined from weighing a cubic foot of the silage. There are reasonably exact formulae for determining this. The heavier the weight per cubic unit the more feed value the silage has.
5. Also the time at which the silage was put up is very important. If the leaves of the corn had started to turn, there would be a substantial drop in potential value.
6. The degree of spoilage, the condition of the silage pit, and the "estimated volume" particularly in a trench silo, when the estimate is being made by the seller, are matters with which an amateur buyer can get in trouble. Estimating the value of silage from a visual inspection requires a real expert.
7. With corn silage it is almost essential that a protein supplement be fed. With a full feed of alfalfa hay, this is usually not necessary.
8. It is generally desirable to have some small amount of a dry ration of either hay or straw when a full silage feed is being used.

4. GRAIN

The principal grains used in the United States for feeding beef cattle are corn, milo, oats and barley. Since the advent of the government's price support program on wheat, it is rarely used.

In the case of all the grains a substantial increase in feed value is obtained if the grain kernel is crushed, cracked or crimped in some manner to break down its exterior wall to permit the digestive juices of the animal to reach it in the event it is swallowed whole. This is not as much of a problem with young calves as it is with older animals who don't chew as well.

While grain forms the principal ration of cattle being fattened on a dry lot, it is generally used only as a supplement for breeding stock cattle. Principally it is used for young calves and occasionally for bulls several months prior to being put out with the cow herd. For animals on a growing rather than fattening ration, a grain supplement of more than two to five pounds per day would be extremely unusual.

Each type of grain has varying species, different degrees of moisture content, varying degrees of spoilage and foreign matter, and several other factors that determine its "grade" and consequent price on the various central grain markets. A grain "futures" market (Chicago is the principal one in the United States) is a means by which big feeders, feed companies, and food processing companies can protect themselves against violent price changes. Through big, financially responsible grain dealers the Podunk Feed Company in Emporia can contract for a hundred carloads of No. 2 yellow corn to be delivered at a given month at a given railroad siding at a given price. They are afraid that the price might go up prior to the time that they need the grain.

On the other hand, the John Doe Grain Elevator Company of Kansas City is nervous about their oversupply of grain in storage and the need to handle the supplies that will be coming in from their country customers. They think the price is going to go down. The Podunk Feed Company buys "futures"; the Doe Elevator Company sells them. The transactions are handled by the grain dealer.

By turning to the section on "Grain Futures" on the financial page of any major newspaper you can see what people anticipate the various classes of grain will be bought and sold for during the various months of the coming year.

With the federal government price support programs on the major grains, a lot of the romance has been taken out of futures trading. Everyone knows that the price cannot fall radically below the government's support level and likewise they suspect that if the price should go substantially higher than the government's level, that the government would start to dump the many billions of dollars worth of surplus that they have on hand in order to cut down their storage charges.

Consequently, with the elimination of the danger of radical price fluctuations, most of the protective "hedging" operations of the past are unnecessary. This has resulted in a substantial decline in futures trading. For example, a seat on the Chicago Board of Trade sold for about $65,000 in 1928 and it is now going for about $6,000.

5. CONCENTRATES

It has been found that small amounts of concentrated proteins added to a cattle ration not only have feed value in themselves but also help in the digestibility of other elements in the ration.

"A study [of the following table] discloses the fact that older animals require less protein in proportion to their live weight than do young animals. This is to be expected, since the rate of growth decreases with age and protein is primarily for growth. Theoretically two-year-old steers on full feed should require still less protein per thousand pounds live weight than the younger animals on somewhat limited rations. However, experimental feeding trials have shown that if a nutritive ratio becomes too wide the efficiency of the entire ration is noticeably lower. Consequently, an increase in the carbohydrate part of the ration requires an accompanying increase in the protein component. Apparently a deficiency in the ration tends to depress the digestion of non-protein substances, probably partly through a lack of sufficient protein for the growth of the fermenting bacteria of the digestive tract. Steers fed shelled corn and timothy hay at the Ohio Station digested only 48.4% of the dry matter of the timothy hay but 54.6% when the ration was supplemented with 2.4 pounds of soybean meal."[2]

PROTEIN REQUIREMENTS OF BEEF CATTLE[3]

	DAILY REQUIREMENTS PER HEAD*		CALCULATED DIGESTIBLE PROTEIN REQD.	
	Digestible Protein (pounds)	*Total Digestible Nutrients (pounds)*	*Daily per 1,000 Lbs. Live Wt.*	*Ratio of Protein to Carbohydrates (nutritive ratio) 1:*
1. Calves fattened for baby beef				
400 pounds	1.05-1.15	7.4- 8.6	2.6 2.9	6.1-6.5
600 pounds	1.26-1.37	10.2-11.8	2.1-2.3	7.1-7.6
800 pounds	1.52-1.68	12.6-14.4	1.9-2.1	7.3-7.6
2. Fattening yearling cattle				
600 pounds	1.18-1.32	10.7-12.3	1.9-2.2	8.0-8.3
800 pounds	1.52-1.68	14.1-15.9	1.9-2.1	8.3-8.6
1,000 pounds	1.71-1.91	16.0-18.0	1.7-1.9	8.4-8.6
3. Fattening of 2-year-old steers				
800 pounds	1.46-1.62	14.1-15.9	1.8-2.0	8.6-8.8
1,000 pounds	1.65-1.85	16.5-18.5	1.6-1.8	9.0
1,200 pounds	1.70-1.90	17.0-19.0	1.4-1.6	9.0

*From Morrison, *Feeds and Feeding*, 21st edition, 1948, p. 1149.

[2]*Beef Cattle*, Rosco R. Snapp, 4th edition, John Wiley & Sons, Inc., New York, 1952, pp. 311-312.

[3]*Idem*, p. 312.

The most common protein concentrates now in general use are cottonseed meal, soybean meal, linseed meal, and dehydrated alfalfa meal. The first three have protein percentages running from 37 to 45%. Alfalfa meal's protein content runs generally from 18 to 22% if the alfalfa was cut in the bloom stage of maturity.

At a cost usually running from $3 to $5 per ton extra, most of these concentrates can be pelletized into a small pellet for calves or a larger pellet for cows. The principal advantage of this is that it can be fed on the ground and a large series of feed bunks do not have to be purchased. In the case of alfalfa meal, the meal is so fine that if fed by itself in a meal form a considerable wind-loss would occur.

Most of the popular commercial manufactured feeds in the United States have mixtures of one or more of these basic elements together with grain, molasses, corncob meal, or something cheaper.

Very often the commercial feed companies will guarantee the total amount of protein in their feed and will identify the general sources but will keep as a closely guarded secret the proportions of each that is contained. One reason for this is that they now have the legal freedom to vary their proportion according to whichever protein supplement is cheapest on the market at that time. This is one reason that batches of the same patented feed seem to have slightly different results when bought at different times.

For a quarter of a century there has been a violent difference of opinion between some of the feed companies and some of the universities on whether or not the mixing of several protein sources in a manufactured feed brings an advantage to the animal over and beyond the normal protein found in a single base feed.

"Mixed feed salesmen place much emphasis upon the fact that by thus combining feeding stuffs a much better quality of protein is obtained, inasmuch as the amino acid deficiencies of one feed are supplemented by the amino acids present in the others. Frequently the claim is made that the 12 or 18% of protein present in a mixed feed is in reality more efficient than the much larger amount of protein in linseed or cottonseed meal fed alone, owing to the lack of certain essential amino acids in the ration when a single protein supplement is fed. This argument fails to recognize that the protein compounds eaten by cattle are broken down and resynthesized by the rumen bacteria before they are digested and assimilated by the cattle. Consequently, the quality of protein fed appears to be of relatively little importance in beef cattle rations. This viewpoint is supported by the results of experiments carried out at the Wisconsin and Kansas stations,

Weaned calves can weigh from 300 to 600 pounds. Animals fitted for show are often brought to heavier weights. (Courtesy, American Hereford Assn.)

In Wyatt Earp's day they dragged a calf out with a rope and two men held it down. Now many places brand in a special squeeze shoot. For a small investment in simple equipment, labor cost per animal is cut in half. A crew of eight men divided into two teams of four with modern equipment can work 2,000 calves per day. (Courtesy, American Hereford Assn.)

Cowboys of the XIT on a roundup in 1895. At that time wages of $15 per month with food and a bunk were par for the course. Today, wages start at $300 per month with considerable fringe benefits. (Courtesy, Rita Blanca Studio, Dalhart, Texas)

California land has gone so high and the competition from the dairy industry is so severe that most breeding herds are limited to registered pedigreed animals, as shown in this famous Angus herd near Fresno. (Courtesy, American Angus Assn.)

The Kansas "Blue Stem" or "Flint Hill" has an underlying limestone which gives the grass a special protein quality. (Courtesy, American Hereford Assn.)

A typical Iowa farm where the operator is marketing his corn by converting it to beef. (Courtesy, American Angus Assn.)

A Pennsylvania farm where land and feed are too expensive to be competitive with the western ranges on any but pedigreed show cattle. (Courtesy, American Angus Assn.)

Giant Allis-Chalmers combines harvesting wheat near Oakley, Kansas. These three machines can equal the work done by two thousand men a century ago. (Courtesy, American Angus Assn.)

in which none of the protein mixtures used proved significantly superior to linseed meal."[4]

The protein content of concentrates doesn't tell the full story as there are other elements that also have a value to the animal. In particular, dehydrated alfalfa meal prepared under the proper conditions could have an abundance of vitamin A. If shipping and handling costs are not a big element, the bulk qualities of the dehydrated alfalfa may have some merit if hay itself is expensive in the area.

6. MINERALS, VITAMINS AND ANTIBIOTICS

Salt is the most necessary element of this group and is normally consumed at a rate of from one to three pounds per head per month, depending on the size of the animal and the season. More is consumed on pasture than on a dry lot and more in the early spring than later in the summer.

In the arid pastures of the West, salt is often mixed with cottonseed meal and left in bunks on a free-choice basis as a method of controlling the intake of protein supplement. Normally this is done on a basis of 3:1, three parts protein to one part salt, and on mature cows this usually gets an average consumption of the mixture running from two to three pounds per day. When the salt content is raised to a 2:1 ratio, there is some argument as to whether or not this might have a detrimental effect on the animals. Naturally it is absolutely necessary that large amounts of good water be available under this type of feeding.

Salt supplies two of the chemical elements needed by cattle, sodium and chlorine. In addition, there are two other essential minerals, calcium and phosphorus. Most farm grains and protein concentrates are relatively good in phosphorus but low in calcium; legume roughages, on the other hand, are excellent sources of calcium but are likely to be low in phosphorus unless they have been grown on phosphorus-rich soils.[5] Steamed bone meal (13-15% phosphorus) and dicalcium phosphate are the usual forms of phosphorus supplement fed. Rock phosphate should not be fed because it usually contains fluorine which is toxic to cattle.

A calcium deficiency can best be corrected by feeding 0.1 pounds daily of limestone flour mixed with the grain ration or scattered over the silage.[6]

---

[4] *Idem*, p. 351.
[5] *Idem*, p. 463.
[6] *Idem*.

Trace minerals such as iron, manganese, copper, sulfur, iodine and cobalt may have some benefit to the rumen bacteria in the cow's stomach and their deficiencies in certain areas of the United States might require the feeding of a mineralized salt.

The more commonly used antibiotics are aureomycin, streptomycin, terramycin and penicillin. When mixed with feeds for cattle that have been recently weaned or shipped or exposed to some unusual weather condition, there is no question but that they may have some effect in preventing disease similar to their use in human beings. However, there is some question as to the advantage of indiscriminately feeding antibiotics when no particular disease situation has been encountered. "Neumann, feeding aureomycin at the Illinois Station to yearling heifers, noted a marked depression of the appetite about 24 hours after the first feeding. This effect continued for about 10 days, after which the consumption of feed by the test cattle gradually increased until it regained the level of the control lot.

"In view of the important role played by bacteria in the digestion of feed by cattle especially the bacteria and protozoa of the paunch, it is doubtful that the feeding of antibiotics to cattle will be a profitable practice."[7]

Vitamin A is required by all animals, but an abundance of it is received on green pasture and is stored in the body tissues. Dehydrated alfalfa hay put up at the proper time has an abundance of carotene, which is its principal source. Usually the first symptom of vitamin A deficiency is night blindness. If this condition is suspected, the cattle should be driven about in twilight or moonlight to see if they have difficulty in avoiding large objects that lie in their path. Subsequent symptoms are muscular incoordination, staggering gate, and excessive running of the eyes and nose caused by the inflammation of the epithelial membranes of these organs.[8]

The best source of vitamin A for cattle suffering from a deficiency is a commercial vitamin A supplement, made from fortified cod-liver oil. One-fourth to one-half ounce of such supplement per day, depending upon the age and size of the animal, should correct the deficiency over a period of about 10 days.[9]

7. RATIONS

As mentioned previously, a winter feed ration depends on what you are trying to do and the class of animal with which you are dealing.

---

[7]*Idem*, pp. 468-469.
[8]*Idem*, pp. 470-471.
[9]*Idem*, p. 472.

To take a healthy 1,000 pound 4-year old cow from October to April after she has had her calf weaned off of her in October and with the expectation of her recalving in May, the following daily rations would be adequate to keep her on a healthy maintenance schedule:

Ration I	*Ration II*	*Ration III*
10 lbs. top alfalfa hay	20 lbs. corn silage	15 lbs. poor oats hay
3 lbs. corn	5 lbs. alfalfa hay	5 lbs. corn
1 lb. cottonseed cake	2 lbs. cottonseed cake	2½ lbs. cottonseed cake

In the preceding three examples it is assumed that a certain amount of rough pasture is available and that we are dealing with an area comparable to Northern Missouri.

In the event that we moved further West, and had more cured dry grass pasture available, these rations could be cut in half during the period the ground was not covered with snow.

If the cattle went into the winter in a heavy fleshy condition, the grain could probably be entirely eliminated from the above ration with a slight increase in the roughage portion.

Rations like the three just described should be varied according to daily conditions. For example, if there is a reasonable pasture, the rations should be cut down 30% when there is no snow cover and increased 30% when there is. The best and greenest part of the alfalfa hay should be reserved for the very end of the winter feeding season when the vitamin A that had been stored by the animal from the preceding summer's pasture would start to go down. Likewise, it is commonly thought to be a good idea to start increasing the protein ration 30 days prior to the time the cow is about to calve so as to help stimulate future milk production.

"The vitamin D requirement of beef cattle is estimated to be 300 IU per 100 pounds of live weight based upon experimental results with calves. Under usual conditions of management, beef cattle receive sufficient vitamin D from exposure to direct sunlight or from sun-cured hay.

"Deficiency of vitamin D in calves reared under controlled experimental conditions results in rickets similar to that occurring in the young of other species of livestock. Clinical symptoms are usually preceded by a decrease in blood calcium and inorganic phosphorus. This is usually followed by poor appetite, decrease in growth rate, digestive disturbances, stiffness in gait, labored breathing, irritability, weakness, and occasionally tetany and convulsions. Later, enlargement of the joints, slight arching of the back, bowing of the legs, and erosion of the joint surfaces cause additional pain and difficulty in locomotion. Posterior paralysis may follow fracture of vertebrae. Symptoms develop more slowly in older animals. Work with dairy cattle has shown that vitamin D deficiency in the pregnant animal may result in dead, weak, or deformed calves at birth.

"The quantitative vitamin E (alpha-tocopherol) requirement of beef cattle has not been critically measured, but it is tentatively estimated to be less than 40 milligrams of alpha-tocopherol per 100-pound calf per day. Under most conditions, natural feedstuffs supply adequate quantities of alpha-tocopherol for adult cattle; however, muscular dystrophy in calves has been reported in certain geographical areas. The signs of alpha-tocopherol deficiency, termed muscular dystrophy or white muscle disease, appear in calves between the ages of 2 and 12 weeks. The most common signs of a deficiency are heart failure and paralysis varying in severity from a slight lameness to complete inability to stand. A dystrophic tongue often is seen in affected animals.

"Dietary requirements for B vitamins (thiamine, biotin, niacin, pantothenic acid, riboflavin, and vitamin B_{12}) have been demonstrated experimentally for the young calf during the first 8 weeks of life, prior to the development of a functioning rumen. These requirements in practice are usually adequately met by milk supplied the calf by the beef cow during early lactation. Following this early age, B vitamins appear to be synthesized in sufficient quantities in most feeding regimens by rumen bacterial fermentation, so that no dietary B vitamins need be supplied to cattle. Unusual feeding conditions, however, such as severe inadequacy of protein or other nutrients in the cattle ration, may impair rumen fermentation to such an extent that sufficient quantities of B vitamins for meeting the animal's needs will not be synthesized. Such deficiencies, if they occur, have not been clearly defined in beef cattle production.

"Although vitamin K is synthesized in the rumen of cattle in adequate amounts under most feeding conditions, symptoms of inadequacy occur when the dicumarol content of hay is excessively high. Moldy sweet clover hay has been shown at times to be high in dicumarol, resulting in a bleeding syndrome through the body, called sweet clover poisoning or bleeding disease. Most effective treatment of this disease is administration of menadione (vitamin K_3) and removal of the offending feed from the cattle ration."[10]

---

[10]*Nutrient Requirements of Domestic Animals*, Number IV, Subcommittee on Beef Cattle Nutrition, National Academy of Sciences—National Research Council, 1958, pp. 18-19.

Chapter IV

Comparison of Geographic Areas

In this section, it should be understood that many different types of land and cattle operations can be found within a single state. The type operation described may not even be typical of 50% of the grazing area of the particular district discussed, but was selected as being of general interest to the reader. Again, even within the same district, the type operation may vary from year to year according to the moisture conditions, the price of different kinds of feeds, the government support program, the introduction of mechanized equipment, changes in the labor market, etc. Prices and costs are generally based on the situation in the years of 1953 through 1959, which may not be typical of the future. The early part of this period involved extreme drought and the latter part heavy restocking.

In Chapter XII it is shown that 500 cows on Kansas blue stem cost $92/head. To equate "maintenance costs" with this figure let us assume the cattle owner is leasing his ranch, furnishing his own bulls, hiring or personally furnishing one-half of the "top management," and paying his own personal property taxes and veterinary bills. By excluding these costs from the $92/head figure, we arrive at a $74 "maintenance cost" for all items excluding depreciation on the cows.

Texas, Arizona, and New Mexico: The preponderance of grazing land has sparse vegetation with anything from 20 to 50 acres being necessary to support a cow. Water is generally a problem. The grass that does exist is of a particularly nutritious quality and cattle stay in good condition on what looks like very little feed. Over most of the area, grazing exists all year long and winter feeding is not a matter of importance. Toward the southern limit, the best grass comes in the winter. Supplementary feeding usually consists of cottonseed cake. Year round maintenance on a cow runs around $60.00. There is no blizzard risk, but the chance of a burn-out in a drought is considerable. On the very rough ranges, a 60% calf crop is not considered low. In areas where Mexican laborers are available, costs are not too high. In areas where they are not, good men will cost $300.00 per month.

California: The tremendous agricultural and urban developments here have caused the price of all land to go so high that it is almost impossible for a commercial rancher to buy a ranch and make any return on his investment. Leases are high and hard to find. The grazing season is the reverse of most of the country, starting in October and burning out in June.

June, July, August, and September are the months that you have to feed hay or whatever supplement you have. Good ranches in the Santa Ynez valley north of Santa Barbara will handle about one cow to ten (10) acres. South of Los Angeles conditions are similar to Arizona and New Mexico. Water is the main problem and many ranches sell off their cattle prior to summer so there is no risk of having to haul it. One month of water hauling can finish off the year's profit. In the Santa Ynez valley, year round maintenance will run around $70.00 if you can avoid excessive summer hay feeding. In the Camp Pendleton area, you are down to $60.00, but the results are not so good.

The labor situation north of Los Angeles is tough. Around San Diego it is a little better.

Wyoming, Idaho, and Montana: Averaging out a huge ranch with the number of cattle it will support gives a considerable number of acres to support a cow. However, the grass that is available is concentrated in small fertile valleys and the cattle can get the concentrated feeding that puts on weight. Blizzards hit during the winter, but there is usually ample timber or shelter for protection. Grazing seasons are short and winter feeding is costly. Water is rarely a problem. On the rough lands, calf crop percentages are not so good. Annual maintenance on a cow now runs around $70.00 and fluctuates directly with the price of hay from district to district, which is the main element of cost.

Western Slope Colorado: This area produces the finest cattle in the country, but is an area of high costs. Hay and cottonseed cake are the main elements of winter feed. In some areas hay went to $45.00 per ton or higher in 1953, which forced the liquidation of some herds. With a rough winter, annual maintenance could run around $80.00. Despite the relatively short grazing season, many ranchers can wean their spring calves at 475 pounds which speaks for the quality of the grass. Most forms of cattle disease are unknown in this area. Water is no problem.

Kansas, Oklahoma, and Eastern Colorado: A good part of this area is the famous "blue stem" country where the grass grows over lime deposits and has an extremely high protein content. A good hot August sun will burn it out, however. Many owners are in the business of renting out pasture at so much per head of cattle for the grazing season to the big ranchers from Texas. Formerly, the owners used to guarantee water on the lease and this almost broke a number of them in 1952 and 1953 with the result that the lessee now generally has to take the gamble. During the winter it is often possible to rent winter wheat fields for grazing, which is a very cheap way of cutting down the winter feed bill. Annual costs on a cow run around $65.00, but they could be $15.00 more or less than this figure depending on the rainfall conditions and the amount of competition for the pastures. Prior to the September rains water is always a problem and August is usually a touch and go situation in this regard. Many of the panics on the Kansas City market have been caused by sudden, large liquidations of Kansas and Oklahoma herds through lack of water. In some areas it is common to leave hay in rolled bales on the field where it is mowed and to turn cattle on this for winter pastures. This cuts out most of the labor in the winter feeding.

Nebraska and South Dakota: In the "Sand Hill" country, you have an interesting situation. The porosity of the soil is such that even in a dry year, which happens frequently here, the soil retains what little rain that falls so you don't have a complete grass failure as you would under a more compact soil condition. Stock water is usually available if you want to sink a well fifty (50) feet. Winter feeding is usually done with rolled bales of hay left on the field supplemented with about 2 pounds of cottonseed cake a day. Ten (10) acres will support a cow and our operations up here have been hitting calf crop percentages of around 90%. Maintenance runs around $60.00. The labor situation is good and you can get cow hands at $180.00 per month. There is a considerable element of blizzard risk, but some of this can be minimized by taking the proper precautions, such as having tractors and sledges ready to haul in feed.

This area, particularly where Indian Bureau leases are concerned, is rapidly seeing an increase in land rents, both government and private.

Missouri, Iowa, and Illinois: This is the center of the "corn belt" and is generally more associated with feeders than breeding herds. This is the area of small farms which handle the registered breeding herds that produce the bulls that are later shipped to the western ranges. Operating costs and pasture leases are high, but the cattle come out big and heavy and 90% calf crops on small carefully supervised farms are not unusual. Corn silage is one of the principal winter feeds. The grazing of winter corn fields after the mechanical picker has missed two bushels an acre is a common, cheap way of getting winter feed. Here, operating costs on a grade animal will run $75.00, and on a registered animal which has to be handled in herds of less than 30, around $90.00.

Florida: Much of this land is handled like that in other sections, but one particular program in recent years deserves special mention. In the past, the so-called tropical grass meadows in the "muck" country looked like a terrific feed situation, but the cattle never put on any weight. However, they are now trying a concentrated fertilizer program which is poured on all during the year and are getting excellent results. By this method, which is expensive, they can get one acre to support a cow and can handle a tremendous herd on a fairly limited ranch. Naturally, there is no winter feeding problem and no water or moisture problem.

Actually, the big problem is drainage and you have public drainage districts similar to the irrigation districts of the West. Outside of the special fertilizer problem you often have the maintenance on the drainage pumps, expensive drainage assessments, ditch repairs and other costs unique to this particular section. Many of the tropical grasses in Florida are not frost resistant and a killing frost such as occurred in 1958 creates a first rate crisis.

Annual maintenance on a packaged deal for an outsider can be found at around $70.00 per head with the owner furnishing his own bulls. Throughout the entire South, by-products of rice, such as husks, are used in various forms of supplementary feeds.

It is generally believed in this area that the tropical heat and humidity require the cattle to have some mixture of Brahma blood to do well. The crossbred Brangus, Santa Gertrudis, and Charbray are currently in vogue.

Northeastern United States: Here most available grazing lands are tied up with dairy herds supplying milk for the big eastern cities. Costs are usually prohibitive for beef cattle or breeding herds outside of small registered show herds.

Chapter V

The Chapter of Accidents

Events which can cause the actual death of livestock or such deterioration that they would have to be liquidated at a fraction of normal value can be divided into the following general classifications:

1. Contagious Diseases
2. Individual Illnesses
3. Preventable Accidents
4. Normal Accidents
5. Theft
6. Acts of God

1. CONTAGIOUS DISEASES

Communicable diseases in cattle as well as humans run the complete gambit from baccilli, amoebae, and filterable viruses, to worms. Also, as in humans, they can be transmitted through flies, ticks, water, food, air, skin contact, and sexual intercourse.

Most can be treated or prevented by inoculation or vaccination. Some respond to sulfa, penicillin, and aureomycin. Others are still being worked on in the research laboratories.

Some are peculiar to certain geographic areas or climatic conditions. Others are peculiar to certain age groups, e.g., nursing calves.

The following are some of the most common or well known:

A. *Bangs Disease* (Brucellosis)—Bangs disease is a highly contagious disease carried by a specific germ, Brucella Abortis, which is most clearly evident in a herd by cows prematurely aborting their young. It can be transmitted at the feed trough, by cows licking the aborted foetus of a carrier, by sexual intercourse between a carrier cow and a clean bull or vice versa.

The germs can stay alive for a number of months during the cold season in moist mud conditions, in manure, particularly in the situation found around feed lots. Four to five hours in the direct sunlight will kill them, however.

Abortion may occur at any time during pregnancy. If the abortion occurs at an early stage, the owner may not be aware that Bangs is present in the herd.

There are varying stages of virulence and it is often possible that a herd may have a low degree of incidence for a period of time but with actual abortions showing up in volume only after a new carrier has been introduced. It is also quite possible as is the case with typhoid in human beings that an animal may be a carrier but still seem to be unaffected itself and continue to produce normal calves.

It is quite common that animals having this infection become barren so that they do not conceive readily or they do not conceive at all.

A test will detect approximately 90% of the carriers and these are what is known as "positive reactors." The other 10% appear as borderline cases or "suspects." The normal practice is to ship your positive reactors and sort off your suspects, retesting them at a later date. Actual reactors will usually show up at that time.

One problem is that in a herd that has been vaccinated against Bangs, particularly when the animals have been vaccinated after eight months of age, a few "suspects" may turn up that are the result of the vaccination and not actual carriers.[1]

There has been a major program by the federal government to wipe out this disease and it is being done on a county by county basis through the country. Some states such as Arizona and New Mexico have almost completely eradicated the disease. Naturally, once an area has been "certified Bangs free," rigid regulations have to be taken before any new cattle are brought in so as to prevent the reintroduction of the disease.

By the use of both federal and state funds, vaccinations and testing are done free. Condemnation awards are also often made to owners who ship Bangs reactors to market. This is normally the difference between what the animal would be worth as a breeding cow and what it brings as a slaughter animal.

B. *Tuberculosis* in cattle is not exactly the same strain as the germ that infects man, but man can catch the cattle variety. Cattle Tuberculosis has been almost entirely stamped out in the United States. It can be transmitted by either food or air, and it can affect the lungs, intestines, brain or other sections of the body.

---

[1] *Animal Sanitation and Disease Control*, R. R. Dykstra, The Interstate Printers & Publishers, Inc., Danville, Ill., 1955, pp. 621-628.

There are three methods of testing for tuberculosis with a tuberculin; (1) in the eye, (2) by temperature, and (3) the most common, the "tail test." A small amount of tuberculin is injected between the layers of the skin directly under the tail. Seventy-two hours later if the animal is infected a swelling will be manifested at the site of injection.[2]

C. *Blackleg* is due to a specific gas-forming germ to which young cattle between the ages of six months and two years are most susceptible, although older animals may contract it. The spore stage of the germ can live for years in soil. It is usually taken into the animal's body with contaminated water. The first noticeable symptom is lameness, which rapidly increases in severity until the animal goes down. Almost simultaneously the affected portion of the body becomes swollen. When the hand is passed lightly over these regions there is imparted a crackling sensation due to the presence of bubbles of gas beneath the skin.

Malignant oedema, an entirely different germ, often gives the identical symptoms.

Consequently, there is now a double vaccination against both diseases which seems to be almost 100% effective. Usually after two years a natural immunity sets in. The routine vaccination of calves against this disease is done almost universally within the United States, both in farm and ranch country.[3]

D. *Texas Tick Fever* was historically the cause of many a gun battle in the early days of the West. When the big herds of Longhorns, which had developed a natural immunity to it, were being herded up the trails into Kansas and Nebraska, the British beef and dairy stock of the homesteaders and farmers dropped like flies. The settler squads, armed with rifles, guarded the sides of the trails in "shotgun quarantines."

This "southern cattle fever" is still presently generally limited to the southern United States. The Southern Fever Tick bears the protozoa that causes the disease. Even when away from cattle the tick hatched from eggs can still cause the disease. To clean out an area, there has to be a period of 66 days in which no infected cattle are in the district. Cattle can be cleaned of ticks by dipping them twice in an approved

---

[2]*Idem,* pp. 639-641.
[3]*Idem,* pp. 594-596.

arsenical dip. There should be a minimum of seven to ten days between the two dippings.[4]

The protozoa causing southern cattle fever infests the blood and causes the red cells to break down so that the red matter gets into the blood plasma and thence in part to the urine, consequently causing the name "red water," which is frequently applied to this disease.

Most native cattle, as mentioned before, can become immune to the disease but imported cattle usually get it in a fatal form. The symptoms in an acute form usually consist of a high temperature, rapid pulse and breathing, pale and yellowish mucous membranes, and discolored urine varying from a light red to almost black. Young animals less than one year of age usually recover, older ones die in approximately 50% of the cases. Blood of a recovered animal remains permanently infected.

It is interesting that the discovery of its transmission by the United States Bureau of Animal Husbandry was instrumental in the discovery of the transmission of such human ailments as malaria and yellow fever.[5]

E. *Anthrax* is a highly dangerous disease that can hit all warm-blooded animals including man. It is caused by the Bacillus Anthracis, a spore forming organism that can live permanently in the soil. In cattle or sheep, death can take place in a few minutes up to two or three hours. There are slower forms of the disease which cause swellings of the lower parts of the body and high fever.

Anti-anthrax serum is fairly effective. Vaccination against the disease is of some value but not 100% effective. Anthrax bactrin will protect herds for approximately one year. There is an attenuated anthrax-spore vaccine which should be used only in herds where the disease has made its appearance and when the occupied pastures are known to be contaminated. This can cause numerous secondary complications and should be used only with professional advice. Penicillin and sulfonamide can inactivate germs in the blood but it must be applied early in the course of the disease.[6]

A century ago, particularly in certain sections of Europe, this was probably the chief cause of livestock fatalities. The original pioneer

---

[4]*Idem,* pp. 752-754.
[5]*Idem,* pp. 779-781.
[6]*Idem,* pp. 636-637.

in the treatment and prevention of this disease was the Frenchman, Louis Pasteur.

F. *Leptospirosis*—In cattle this disease is due to a spirochete known specifically as Leptospira Pomoma which occurs in the blood, urine, milk and other tissue in early stages of the disease. The first symptoms are when the milk and urine become blood tinged and the visible mucous membranes begin to appear yellowish.[7]

Lack of appetite, loss of weight, and generally poor appearance of hair are quite characteristic. Some mortality can occur and particularly the generally depressed condition of the cattle can make them more susceptible to other diseases. Recovery usually takes several months. Even after recovery apparently healthy animals can be carriers. Antibiotics are fairly effective and there has recently been introduced a vaccine which seems to be pretty good.[8]

Animals with the disease should be separated from the herd and kept separate for a couple of months after recovery. New animals coming into the herd should always be kept sorted off for a few weeks for observation. This is important not only for this disease but for many others.

G. *Hemorrhagic Septicemia*—This disease is also known as "shipping fever of cattle," "stockyards fever," "stockyards pneumonia," or "lung fever." The germ is normally found in the respiratory and digestive tracts of animals and is very susceptible to the action of the mildest disinfectants. It is usually found as a mild almost harmless organism but for reasons not clearly understood it suddenly flares up. This possibly is caused by the lower resistance from the strain and rigors of being shipped, change in surroundings, change in food supply after being weaned and other environmental factors. The most common form is lung fever with chilling, high temperature, difficult breathing, and coughing. It can be found in an intestinal form with bloody diarrhoea and colicky pains. It can attack the throat and cause swelling and in an extreme form, death can result in less than twenty-four hours.

There is a vaccination with a bacterin that can be given to them at least ten days or two weeks before shipping which is a relatively effective immunizing agent. The vaccination after the disease has

[7] *Idem*, p. 580.
[8] *Idem*.

advanced is not too effective. There is an anti-hemorrhagic septicemia serum which is somewhat helpful in the curative treatment. Separating "suspects" from the balance of the herd is the best way of limiting its spread. Antibiotics are also effective.

H. *Anaplasmosis*–This is also known as the yellow teat disease and is an ailment affecting both young and aged cattle. It is believed to be due to an animal parasite, a protozoa known as the Anaplasma Marginale which affects the red blood cells. The disease can be transmitted from animal to animal by means of biting insects and mechanical agencies such as bleeding needles, hypodermic needles, dehorning and other surgical instruments. Animals which have this disease may be permanent "carriers" and are potential sources of danger to others.

The disease adversely affects the flow of milk, causes marked rise in temperature, and semi-collapse. Very young calves are seldom if ever fatally affected.

At the moment, there is no positive means of detecting a carrier but the U. S. Bureau of Animal Husbandry is testing a device which looks like it will be successful. In areas of the country where the disease is endemic, consideration can be given to inoculating calves shortly after birth with some virulent blood. Calves so inoculated will become lifetime carriers but the herd itself will be relatively immune. Some of the antibiotics seem to be fairly successful in overcoming the "carrier state" but the animals so treated again become susceptible.[9]

It is now suspected that the disease has been almost universally prevalent for generations through the southern parts of the United States and its recent flaring up in the North might be due to the importation of southern cattle. With the inability to detect "carriers," it probably exists to some degree in almost every section of the United States.

I. *Foot and Mouth Disease*–This is a highly contagious disease of cloven hoofed animals such as cattle, swine, sheep, goats, deer and others. Horses do not contract the disease. Man is susceptible to a mild extent. The disease is caused by a filtrable virus which hits the blood, milk and saliva during the fever stage of the disease and causes blisters to occur during the ailment. Blisters on the mouth cause a drooling of saliva and blisters on the feet cause lameness. It

---

[9]*Idem*, pp. 778-779.

is highly contagious and all carcasses have to be destroyed and buried. Actual death in an acute outbreak is not large, generally not being more than 3%. However, in the countries in which the disease is endemic, it accounts for a substantial decrease in milk and meat production.

The federal government has gone to great lengths in tracing down every outbreak with the result that the disease has been almost entirely eradicated in the United States.[10]

Because of failure by various foreign governments to take the same effective measures that we have done, the United States has had to prohibit the importation of live cattle from many parts of the world. Even in areas that are believed to be clean but where the inspection laws are not as severe as our own, we usually require long periods of quarantine before we permit the animals to be released among American herds. There is no question but that the same degree of effort and expense could also effectively stamp out a half dozen other endemic diseases now present in the United States.

2. INDIVIDUAL ILLNESSES

Outside of the general run of heart attacks, malignant and nonmalignant tumors, relatively noncontagious pneumonias, and various ailments connected with old age, the following are some of the more common illnesses associated with beef cattle:

A. *Cancer Eye* is a malignancy involving the eyeball and immediately contiguous tissues. It is most common to Hereford or Whiteface cattle. It is interesting to note that in the Herefords which have a small red rim of segmented skin around the eyelid that there is a relative immunity to this. At the moment this is becoming quite a desirable characteristic in selecting breeding bulls for one's herd.[11]

In more valuable animals, it is feasible to have a veterinary remove the eye and the animal may very well continue its normal life cycle with no further trouble. In less valuable grade herds, the expense is not justified and it is customary to ship the animal to slaughter after it has weaned its calf.

B. *Lump Jaw*—This disease is caused by the entrance into the tissues of the ray-fungus (Actinomyces Bovis) and related organisms. They

---

[10] *Idem*, pp. 647-653.
[11] *Idem*, p. 474.

usually enter the tissues through the wounds of recently erupted teeth or through injuries in the mouth from other causes. It may even be inhaled into the lungs. In the region of the head in cattle, it causes swelling of either the bone of the jaw or of the neighboring soft tissues. In the tongue it can cause an enlargement, sometimes with ulcers, and loss of mobility so that the animal is said to have "wooden tongue."

Surgical handling consists of lancing of the abscesses so as to liberate the thick yellow pus contained therein. Medical treatment is used either to supplement the surgical treatment or alone when the ailment is in an inoperable region.

Iodine in any of various forms is the most practical destructive agent. In liquid form it may be packed into the wound on gauze saturated with it, or it may be administered by way of the mouth as iodide of potash. Iodide of soda may be injected intravenously. This is not a good idea when animals are in the advanced stages of pregnancy.[12]

In range cattle, it is common to ship all "lump jaw" cows after their calves have been weaned. The intravenous injections usually seem to temporarily check the condition if not to completely cure it, and the cow can usually be carried through the weaning period.

C. *Mastitis of the Udder*—Mastitis is also known as garget or "caked bag." 90% of the cases are caused by a germ known as Streptococcus Agalactiae. It is most common in dairies where it is spread from one cow to another by the milkers. It is relatively uncommon in beef cattle on the range.[13]

It often seems to start from an injury and sometimes only affects one quarter and not the others. In older cows a fibrosis may develop in one teat which could lead to chronic mastitis and occasionally can be cured by surgery. In heifers a thin membrane could obstruct the teat higher up.[14]

D. *Screw Worms*—The primary screw worm can breed only in the tissues of living, warm-blooded animals, and it must depend on finding a wounded or diseased part of the body in which its young can begin development. It is most common in the southern and southwestern states and occasionally gets as far north as Iowa, Illinois and Indiana.

---

[12] *Idem*, pp. 464-466.
[13] *Idem*, p. 612.
[14] *Idem*, p. 477.

A hay baler putting up square bales from wind rows near Strong City, Kansas. (Courtesy, *Kansas Farmer*)

Sorghum crops made into silage can probably produce the maximum weight of feed from a given acre of good soil. (Courtesy, State Board of Agriculture, Topeka, Kansas)

Getting the maximum weight gain from cattle on full feed is a highly technical and skilled operation. (Courtesy, American Angus Assn.)

When the ground is covered with snow you have to double the hay ration. (Courtesy, American Hereford Assn.)

One of the early ancestors of the Hereford breed, "Prize Fighter," painted in 1780 in Herefordshire. (Courtesy, American Hereford Assn.)

"Silver," bred by Benjamin Tompkins, Sr., Herefordshire, 1742. One of the first cows with close to modern Hereford markings. (Courtesy, American Hereford Assn.)

The famous "Anxiety IV." This is probably the principal ancestor of most of the American Hereford lines. (Courtesy, American Hereford Assn.)

Ideal beef conformation in Shorthorn Bull. (Courtesy, American Shorthorn Breeders' Assn.)

In areas with a heavy screw worm problem it is common to postpone branding, castrating, dehorning, etc. until either before or after the screw worm season. For example, in Missouri the season usually starts by May and ends after the first hard frost in September.

The primary screw worm fly is bluish green in color and generally lays its eggs on the edges of a wound. Hatching of the eggs occurs in eleven hours and the young whitish worms immediately burrow under the flesh where they feed and grow for a period of four to seven days. During the larva or maggot stage, the worms shed their skins twice. Subsequently they drop to the ground and form the pupa and after 7 to 60 days the fly emerges. The normal life cycle is completed in 21 days but under cold, unfavorable conditions the cycle takes as many as 80 days.[15]

Continuous average temperatures of 50° or lower for approximately three months will eradicate the fly from any area. It is believed that careful spraying and treatment of animals during the winter with particular care given to the treatment of any wounded animals that might be infested can stop the "winter life cycle" which could go far toward eliminating the pests the following summer.[16]

Numerous chemicals and ointments have been developed recently which seem to be quite effective in stopping screw worm development. When branding or dehorning is necessary during the screw worm season, it is certainly desirable to have extra riders checking the herd to be sure that none of the animals have been affected and to give early treatment for ones that have.

E. *Internal Parasites*—There are well over 100 internal parasites that can cause serious damage to cattle. The most common and most serious ones are the various forms of round worm parasites that attack calves and yearlings in both the intestines and the lungs.

Most parasites are present to a small degree in all cattle and it is usually when the cattle are weak from a change of environment, just having been weaned, or just after shipping, that a flare-up can occur which will increase the number to a point where they cause serious damage. Again the best treatment is to isolate the afflicted animals and to try to create sanitary conditions for them. Wet, muddy, packed-in quarters in a feed lot is the best way of getting in trouble. Rotating pastures is an excellent means of eliminating it as the absence

[15]*Keeping Livestock Healthy*, U. S. Department of Agriculture, 1942, pp. 314-316.
[16]*Idem*, p. 320.

of hosts for a period of time will interrupt the life cycle of the worm. Various forms of chemical medication in pills or drenches are effective. In any case, a microscopic analysis of both the stool and the blood should be made so the source and degree of the trouble can be pinpointed.[17]

F. *Scours* is a general term for various ailments with a symptom of diarrhea. In newborn calves, white scours is a special disease which is the result of infections entering through the navel and the mouth.[18]

Scours in animals over several weeks old are normally due to digestive upsets. In the early spring, when animals which have been on a dry lot to feed all winter are turned out to fresh green pasture, a small degree of scouring will hit all of them. It is particularly common when animals are first weaned and change their diet from milk to grass and other feed that you will get the scouring for a week or two. When calves are weaned a month or two early and then shipped a long distance to entirely new grass and feed conditions, it would be rather unusual not to have a few scouring. It is commonly thought within the industry that heavy quantities of soybean meal for animals that are not used to it will tend to cause scouring.

3. PREVENTABLE ACCIDENTS

As in every such classification, there is a hazy band between what is "preventable" and what is "bad luck."

A. *Hardware*—There is a substantial number of cattle that die every year by getting bits of wire or metal in their feed. This is particularly true of small old midwestern farms that have lots of junk lying around.

B. *Lead, Arsenic, or Other Chemical Poisoning*—This is usually caused by ranchers leaving old cans of paint or spray around. Cattle that are short on salt or minerals are particularly inclined to lick this stuff.

C. *Plant Poisoning*—The most common poisonings from plants which can occur on a large scale are those from bloat and prussic acid. Bloat is commonly caused by cattle getting into an alfalfa or clover field early in the spring or after a rain. The young alfalfa can generate a gas in the stomach which can kill the animal in 30 minutes. After

---

[17] *Idem*, pp. 601-602.
[18] *Animal Sanitation and Disease Control*, R. R. Dykstra, The Interstate Printers & Publishers, Inc., Danville, Ill., 1955, pp. 582.

the summer has progressed and the alfalfa field has dried out and matured, limited amounts of grazing can be done but a careful watch must be kept.

The most common form of prussic acid poisoning is from sudan grass. This is an excellent pasture and forage but it should be carefully watched, particularly after a drouth period, if the soil has been heavily fertilized with nitrates or if a field has been cut for hay and there is a subsequent young second growth. These seem to be indications of danger.

There are numerous other wild seeds and grasses which are poisonous to cattle during certain periods of the year. However, as a general rule, animals that have sufficient other forage in abundance will tend to have a natural instinct to avoid the plants that will hurt them.

Many plants taken exclusively by themselves would be damaging but are perfectly good forage when mixed with other feed in the animal's stomach. For example, if it is desired to graze an alfalfa field, it is usually a good idea to let the cattle fill up on hay or other grasses early in the morning and not open the alfalfa field until around noon. Also, old alfalfa fields that have a substantial amount of other grass growing up with the alfalfa are normally fairly safe.

D. *Drowning*—Cattle will not ordinarily venture into water that they cannot swim out of. The most common occurrence here is in northern climates where stock ponds are frozen over. If, on a given morning, a hole is not chopped in the ice near the bank, young inexperienced cattle may congregate on the middle of the ice. The ice may break from all of the weight and 10 to 15 animals could drown at a crack. Old range cows know about ice and will crack it with their front hooves near the edges.

If a herd is being driven across a swift river, naturally some kind of ford should be selected. Also, some arrangement should be made for new born calves as they won't have the stamina to make it.

E. *Drought*—A good part of the disaster from a major but not complete drought can be mitigated by always having a reserve pasture or reserve supplies of feed available.

While there are undoubtedly a few such people, I personally never heard of a rancher who went broke because he consistently undergrazed his pastures. On the other hand, every bank west of the

Mississippi could name you fifty who went broke because they overgrazed.

4. NORMAL ACCIDENTS

A. *Transportation and Handling*—When a large group is being moved by truck or rail, or when a group is being worked in a corral, some animal is going to get trampled, get pushed through a holding pen, or fall in a loading chute.

While many of these accidents can be corrected by checking equipment ahead of time, not overcrowding, not trying for excessive speed, etc., a certain amount will always occur.

B. *Fighting Bulls*—New bulls brought into a pasture will always fight until a "boss" is determined. There will always be a few injuries but rarely a mortality.

C. *Wolves, Coyotes, and Wild Dogs*—There will be a few new born calves lost to these animals. As soon as they become a nuisance, a hunt has to be organized.

D. *Quicksand, Swamps, Cliffs, and Old Wells*—If a serious hazard exists, these areas can be fenced off. However, there will always be a "freak accident" or two; registered cows hung up by their neck chains, calves trapped in abandoned sheds, cows in an arroyo with cliff banks. Many can be saved by a daily inspection of the herd.

5. THEFT

Cattle rustling on the grand scale largely disappeared with the fenced ranges and state brand inspection stations on every highway. Range detectives and brand inspectors paid by private associations, state groups, and the federal government are on duty at all major stockyards.

Normally in range country the distances are great enough that it would be almost impossible for any major movement to take place that wouldn't be spotted, particularly where any strangers were concerned. In recent years, however, with the advent of the refrigerated truck, a new type of petty rustling has started up which is extremely hard to catch. Here the thieves go out and shoot a couple of animals, butcher them on the spot, leave the hide and put the meat in the freezer. Several major rings have been broken up on this particular device.

In areas of the country where the fences are poor and branding is not customary, it is not too uncommon for a calf or yearling to get into a "neighbor's" pasture and the animal gets hurriedly shipped along with some of the "neighbor's" own cattle. That the hazard is relatively low is evidenced by the fact that in most sections of the country it would be easy to get theft insurance from a major livestock insurance company for less than a 1% premium.

Cattle generally are valuable enough that an individual animal would put a thief in the "Grand Larceny" bracket. In most states he would be likely to find that the local judge and jury were all responsible cattlemen and there would be a remote chance of him getting anything less than two years in the brig.

6. ACTS OF GOD

A. *Lightning*—This can be a serious item in the Great Plains area. There are cases where 50 animals are packed together in a rain storm against a fence. Lightning hits the wire and the entire bunch is electrocuted.

B. *Blizzard*—Blizzard has two effects: (1) actually freezing young animals, particularly new born calves; (2) blocking transportation and covering the ground so that the herd starves to death or gets weakened so it dies of exposure.

The first item can be minimized in northern climates by attempting to breed the herd so that calves will drop after April 1st. A late March or early April blizzard is the one that does the most damage.

In range areas it is always common to save your rugged areas with gulleys and woods for your winter pasture where the cattle can get some wind shelter. Small farms, of course, have no problem with their barns and sheds.

In respect to the feed, it is a good idea to make a detailed reconnaissance of the ranch in the summer, estimating the direction of the prevailing winds and guessing where the cattle would drift. Here, emergency stacks of hay should be set up and fenced off. If a whopper arrived, a man could get in on snowshoes or skiis and open up the stacks.

Big ranches maintain caterpillar tractors and blades to cut a path to marooned stock. Cargo planes could make an air drop as a last resort. Light planes are invaluable for locating them for ground crews.

SUMMARY

Statistical analysis of the causes of death in livestock leaves a lot to be desired. First, farmers and ranchers notoriously hate paper work and are generally disinclined to bother filling out the information reports asked for by the Department of Agriculture. Second, the insurance companies which are pretty good sources of material for most types of casualties in other fields are not too good here because only a very small proportion of beef cattle are ever insured. The ones that are, usually involve conditions of abnormal hazard or animals of high value which are either moved around in the show circuit or have conditions of care and maintenance not common with grade breeding herds.

The following is quoted from a letter dated July 7, 1960, from one of the principal officers of the American Live Stock Insurance Company:

> "We have a pretty good idea of what proportion of cattle die under our own insurance and under Lloyd's, and for that matter, under Hartford. Both American loss ratio and Hartford are available through Best's analysis and I think you'll find that someplace around 55% is the loss ratio against a premium income. Of course, this does not reflect the number of animals that are insured. You can't break that down successfully. The loss ratio from one year to another is so completely different that it leaves an actuary without any ground on which to stand.
>
> "As far as diseases are concerned, that again is something that no one can set up as a pattern. We may have certain times of the year, in particular Spring, when we can expect heavy losses due to pulmonary debility. Animals go through winter, usually giving up a certain amount of their strength over a particularly hard winter and break down and be subject to a variety of diseases which are not necessarily the pulmonary type but still tie in with weakness when spring comes around.
>
> "We can anticipate 'bloat' at a time of the year when green forage may be easily and readily available. Weather conditions change the ground growth so that we may have anaplasmosis in certain areas where we normally would not have it. Or we may have an incidence of 'tick fever' in an area where it has not been prevalent before. After a great many years of this Livestock insurance business, we've decided that to hang your hat on any peg that says these diseases are the most prevalent and these diseases are the least—is closing your mind to the element of chance and the turn of the wheel. What seems to us to be terribly important, as a reason for loss this year may be the least important next year.
>
> "We keep only records, then, for the loss ratio with regards to premium and when we are through it seems to stay fairly consistent and do not try to keep any loss ratio as regards to numbers. I'm afraid that if we did, we would defeat our purpose.
>
> "I'm sorry that we can't be of more help but I think I'm speaking for Lloyd's as well as for ourselves in this kind of opinion. We've endeavored to get from Lloyd's whatever information they have and with all that they do I think they have in facts and figures and statistics even less than we do. This is something that has been a product of practical experience and a general feeling for the conditions of the Livestock producer more

than the feelings of an actuary that has allowed for any individual rate schedule to be established."

Picking a very wild figure out of the air based on my own personal impressions and contacts, I would say that the so-called 3% national average of annual mortalities in beef cattle could be divided as follows: 1% disease, 1% weather conditions, ½% preventable accidents and ½% "Acts of God." There is probably a plus or minus 1% factor where strong, tight management, prior planning, and fast preventative action on the part of the rancher can make itself felt.

PART II

HISTORY AND THE GOVERNMENT

Chapter VI

History of the Breeds

Cattle as we know them today are the result of selection by nature and selection by man. The "Wild Ox" or urus (Bos Primigenius) was hunted during the Pleistocene period by Paleolithic Man. By Cro-Magnon times there were three species in Europe, and the Bos Indicus, the ancestor of the humped Brahma cattle, probably existed in Asia.

Nature, in her survival of the fittest technique, used the following breeding factors:

1. Ability to stand drought and lack of forage.
2. Ability to stand extreme cold.
3. Fighting qualities to stand off predatory animals.
4. Fighting ability of bulls to whip other bulls and maintain possession of a harem of cows.
5. Cunning and hiding ability to outwit the spears and axes of Paleolithic Man.

There seems to be some indication that 20,000 to 25,000 years ago wild cattle were the principal meat element in Stone Age Man's diet. They also played a principal part in his culture and religion similar to the role of the buffalo with the Plains Indian. In the Hall of Bulls in the Lascaux Cave in southern France, there is a considerable series of excellent paintings indicating that wild cattle had already evolved a large number of colors, hair forms, horn shapes, and different body conformations. From the skeleton remains, the Bos Primigenius stood six feet high at the shoulder and often had a horn spread between five and seven feet.[1]

Neolithic Culture which involved the use of polished stone implements rather than chipped stone, the planting of grain, the making of pottery, and the domestication of animals (exclusive of the dog which was probably Paleolithic) evolved somewhere between 6,000 and 10,000 B. C. As to whether it was along the Nile, Danube, Tigris or Euphrates River Valleys or possibly further East, there is a difference of opinion among anthropologists. In any case, by 5000

[1]*The Cattlemen*, Mari Sandoz, Hastings House, New York, 1958, pp. 23-28.

B. C. vast and complicated Neolithic cultures had sprung up along the river valleys in most of the temperate areas of the Old World.

There is little question that Neolithic man quickly understood the principle that you ate the inferior animals and kept the animals that had qualities you desired as the basis of your breeding herd. In addition, they probably understood the principle of castrating all but the most "desirable" bulls and retaining them to transmit the qualities that they wanted.

What did Neolithic Man want?

1. A tractable animal that could be herded along the trail.
2. A powerful ox that could be yoked to a plow or a wagon.
3. A beef animal.
4. An animal that could be milked daily without having to chase it through the woods.
5. A dairy animal that would give lots of milk.
6. A fighting bull that would put on a spectator show for Minos in Crete.
7. A placid animal that could be led in a religious procession in Pre-Dynastic Egypt.
8. All of the hardy-survival, easy-breeding qualities developed in Natural Selection.

By historic times Man started breeding different classes of cattle to meet different specialized needs. "From prehistoric days, Egypt concentrated on the breeding of two animals, the greyhound and a polled, a hornless cattle. In the rock tombs of Deir, dating before 2500 B. C., are many pictures showing the handling of cattle. The tomb of Huy, who was in charge of Tutankhamen's royal herds, portrays his men branding King Tut's cattle, while the tomb of Auta, of the Fifth Dynasty, before 2625 B. C., shows a bull branded 113 on the left rump."[2]

"Some time after 6000 B. C. the lake dwellers of Switzerland had two kinds of domestic ox, the urus and a Celtic shorthorn."[3] By Biblical and Roman times, livestock was the most commonly accepted standard of wealth. Our own word "pecuniary" comes from the Latin word "pecunia," meaning "money," which in turn was derived from the Latin "pecus" for "cattle."

"By 630 B. C., Andalusian cattle were a hardy lot, some used as work oxen but mostly bred for beef. They were descended quite directly from Bos Primigenius, substantially horned, great in stature

[2]*Idem,* p. 27.
[3]*Idem,* p. 28.

and strength, and well adapted to the hot, dry summers. It was this blood that fitted so well into Spanish America."[4]

"Before Hernando Cortez had actually secured the City of Mexico, Spaniards sailing to Vera Cruz in 1521 brought to the shores of North America the first cattle. . . . The hardy and tough-sinewed Spanish cattle, tinged with the savage blood of the fighting bulls of the Plazas, seemed exactly fitted to thrive in the new continent's wilderness. Running wild, they increased enormously."[5]

With slight infusions of French cattle and occasional Missouri work oxen from the British breeds of New England, these wild cattle seemed to tend to throw back to the original European primitive ancestor, the urus. They gradually acquired a many colored but stabilized conformation and became an established breed, the Texas Longhorn. Through natural selection the wild Longhorn developed a phenomenal ability to survive in times of drought. It could graze a radius of 100 miles from water and thrive. In the period where the only way to market your cattle was by a 1,000 mile drive over semi-desert country, the Longhorn had a definite place in history.

By the time of the Civil War, major efforts were being made to crossbreed the native Longhorn stock with the heavy more meaty British beef breeds. First they used Shorthorn bulls, later Hereford and Angus. As the ranges became more settled, and fences could control the breeding, and artificial water and feed facilities were developed, purebred herds of these breeds were introduced that could probably not have survived the rough days of the open range.

Actually, British stock was introduced into New England and Virginia almost from the time of the first settlers but this was before the day of the established British breeds that we now recognize. In England of the 16th Century, cattle had the triple purpose of being milk animals, draught animals, and after they were too old for these functions, being slaughtered for beef. In addition to the basic British stock of varied colors, sizes and conformation there were considerable imports from the Continent from the Saxons on down. Lord Scudamore, who died in 1671, introduced a lot of breeding stock from Flanders which is thought to be one of the basic crosses in the animals around Herefordshire.[6]

The idea of breeding an animal designed to mature early and produce the maximum amount of meat for the least amount of pasture, labor,

---

[4] *Idem*, p. 29.

[5] *The King Ranch*, Tom Lea, Vol. I., Little, Brown and Co., 1957, p. 112.

[6] *The Hereford in America*, Donald R. Ornduff, 1957, p. 7.

and feed regardless of his ability to pull a plow was a new concept that wasn't done on an organized basis until the middle of the 18th Century.

"History records that the systematic improvement of the Herefords was begun by the elder Benjamin Tompkins in 1742. In that year he set forth on a system of breeding that ultimately completely altered the character of the cattle of Herefordshire, becoming the originator of the improved breed, and the pioneer improver of cattle in Great Britain on systematic lines.

"Not one man in a thousand, declared Charles Darwin, the great English naturalist-biologist, possesses that accuracy of eye, touch and judgment necessary to accumulate the slight variations in domestic animals in a given direction, and by constant selection to so fix them as to constitute a distinct variety or breed."[7]

Tompkins and his sons bred for beef and conformation on the Herefords without regard to colors. By the beginning of the 19th Century the Hewer and Jeffries families were breeding bulls that began to attain the standard Hereford appearance of today. Three famous names were Silver, Sovereign, and Cotmore. By this time the competitive English stock shows had started, which probably had as much to do as any other factor in the development of world famous British breeds.[8]

Henry Clay, the prominent statesman from Kentucky, made the first known importation of Herefords into the U. S. in 1816. They were crossed with his Shorthorns and their identity lost. The first substantial import for a regular breeding herd was by William H. Sotham in 1840. The herd eventually became located near Buffalo, New York.[9]

Possibly the most significant import as far as American Hereford bloodlines are concerned was that of Anxiety 4th by the firm of Gudgell and Simpson of Pleasant Hill, Missouri, around 1883. Around 1880 Alex Swan formed the Swan Land and Cattle Company with about $3,000,000 in Scotch capital. Secondarily he formed the Wyoming Hereford Association. This resulted in a mass move of Herefords through the Northern Plains area and eventually through the West.[10]

Colonel Charles Goodnight of the famous JJ and JA brands was probably the principal pioneer in introducing the Hereford to Texas and the Southwest. The foundation of his herds came from Finch,

---

[7]*Idem*, p. 12.
[8]*Idem*, pp. 14-19.
[9]*Idem*, p. 30.
[10]*Idem*, p. 54.

Lord, and Nelson of Burlingame, Kansas, in 1883.[11]

Polled Hereford cattle were developed from mutants born without horns shortly before the end of the 19th Century.

For some reason the principal handicap of this breed for many years was a tendency to have a poorer rear end than the better types of horned Herefords. This has largely been overcome over the last thirty years.

It is interesting to note that in the case of this breed the movement across the Atlantic was reversed and most of the British Polled Hereford stock comes from American imports.

The horns have the disadvantage of causing injuries when cattle are being fed packed in around feed bunks and they generally contribute to fighting and other activities causing a loss of weight gain. For many years it has been the practice in at least the middlewestern areas to dehorn all calves at the spring roundup. This particular process is not only a labor-causing problem but in areas where screw worms are prevalent, a considerable hazard of infection exists right after dehorning

In many areas of the country where climatic conditions force the spring roundup to be held late into screw worm time, the horns have to be left on the calves until after the first frost. If the calf is six or seven months old at that time, the removal of the horns is a fairly severe shock to the system of the animal and it usually takes him about a week to start putting on the normal gain. If this operation, as it often does, comes at the same time as the calf is weaned from its mother, put in a truck and shipped a long distance under poor weather conditions to a feeder, there is an excellent chance that it will be run down enough to pick up shipping fever or any one of a number of other diseases hitting newly weaned animals.

By breeding the horns off instead of cutting them off, this whole problem is eliminated. There seems to be some individual variation as to the abilities of polled bulls to breed off the horns of their progeny when mixed with horned cows. While the polled quality is apparently a dominant gene, there seem to be some additional complexities on breeding polled bulls to horned cow herds. Some bulls are "dehorners" and others are not.

The Shorthorn was one of the first improved breeds to be introduced into this country from England.

It originated in Northeastern England in the counties of Northumberland, Durham, York, and Lincoln. Shorthorns were introduced

---

[11]*Idem*, p. 135.

into the U. S. in 1783 with their importation into Virginia; next they arrived in New York in 1791. Strains of the Shorthorn have been selected for milk and butterfat production as well as beef. In the U. S. they are called Milking Shorthorns; in Canada, Dual Purpose Shorthorns; in England and Australia, Dairy Shorthorns.[12]

The Shorthorn for show purposes can be a variety of colors but the most prominent color in most herds is a uniform roan. It was originally designed to be both a beef animal and a dairy animal. In this age of specialization it gradually had to give way to the specialized beef animals such as Hereford and Angus, and in the dairies to Guernseys, Jerseys and Holsteins. However, in recent years the breed was divided into Beef Shorthorns and Milking Shorthorns, each with its own association, and they seem to be undergoing a moderate comeback. The chart at the end of this chapter shows their present position as far as registered animals are concerned.

Historically in the U. S., they were the first animals to be introduced into the Western Plains to improve the Spanish breeds. Particularly was this true of California and the cattle areas which were populated from California such as eastern Washington and eastern Oregon. In any case they seemed to rapidly give way before the Hereford which was introduced later and it is rather unusual to find a large western commercial ranch stocked with Shorthorns.

There is a considerable body of thought within the industry, however, that believes a small amount of Shorthorn blood introduced into one of the strictly beef breeds has some merit in producing cows that are better milkers and can wean a larger calf.

In the last quarter of a Century their principal merit has been for the small family farm where a single herd is expected to produce both beef and milk. Possibly the biggest single factor causing their decrease in popularity has been the gradual disappearance of the "small family farm." I am personally acquainted with a large number of ranchers in Western Kansas who are running large herds of beef cattle, but their wives invariably get the family milk from the grocery store in the local town. The large dairies, on the other hand, almost always sell out their calves as vealers and rarely try to get into the meat business.

Angus are presently on the upgrade through the U. S. They are all black in the adult but often a dark brown as a new born calf. They do not have horns and have a smaller head than a Hereford. Some Hereford breeders use Angus bulls on their first calf heifers because of a belief that the smaller head on the calf will make delivery easier.

---

[12]*Encyclopaedia Britannica*, Volume 5, 1958, p. 47.

Some of the first Angus cows in the United States. Picture taken on XIT Ranch in 1898. (Courtesy, Rita Blanca Studio, Dalhart, Texas)

Registered Angus females from a show herd at Pleasant Plains, Illinois. (Courtesy, American Angus Assn.)

The famous three-fourths Brahma and one-fourth Angus "Chief of Chetopa" owned by Mr. L. L. Clymer of Marion, Ohio. This animal bred to registered Angus females produces "certified" Brangus of the required five-eighths—three-eighths cross. (Courtesy, American Brangus Assn.)

The Brangus may be becoming the most popular of the cross breeds, being without horns and having the tropical adaptability of the Brahma. Officially they are five-eighths Angus and three-eighths Brahma. (Courtesy, American Brangus Assn.)

Richard King (1824-1885), the famous steamboat captain and founder of the King Ranch. (Courtesy, *The Cattleman,* Fort Worth, Texas)

Roundup on a Texas ranch in the 1890s. (Courtesy, Rita Blanca Studio, Dalhart, Texas)

Grass and water in the big range country. (Courtesy, American Hereford Assn.)

This is probably correct.

This breed of black polled beef cattle commonly called "doddies" originated in the county of Aberdeen, Scotland. Its ancestry is obscure. The breed was improved and the present type of the cattle fixed early in the 19th Century by a number of constructive breeders among whom Hugh Watson and William McCombie were the most famous. This breed was introduced into the U. S. in 1873 and after that its influence spread widely in this and other countries.[13]

Purebred Brahmas have not gone through the scientific 100 year old beef breeding selection of the other three breeds. Consequently, the purebred Brahma herds are rarely an end in themselves but are kept to furnish bulls for crossbreeding.

The Brahman (Zebu) term was selected by the U. S. Department of Agriculture as the name of all breeds of Indian cattle in the United States. In South America and in Europe these are known as Zebus. Humped cattle of India were imported into the U. S. as early as 1849, but the importations that had the widest influence were made in 1906 and in 1921. These cattle were used in the gulf coast area of the U. S. for crossing with the improved breeds of beef cattle to produce a type adapted to the hot, humid conditions prevailing in that region. This breed is characterized by a hump above the shoulders, extreme development of loose pendulous skin under the throat, on the dewlaps, navel and the sheath of the males.[14]

Generally when crossbred to British stock, they transmit to the offspring their resistance to tropical diseases, ticks, heat, and swampy conditions. Among their other unusual characteristics, their skin has a sweating ability, so that the evaporation of the moisture has a cooling effect which enables them to thrive and put on weight under heat conditions that cause the other breeds to deteriorate.

The primary cross of Brahmas on other stock usually gives offspring bigger than either parent from the characteristic heterosis or "hybrid vigor" factor. However, secondary crosses usually revert to parent size. Another disadvantage of the primary cross is the usual extreme irregularity of conformation and color in the results. This has been particularly noticeable in Florida. Feeders, who like uniformity and who are afraid of "culls from a dairy herd," will dock these animals 3c a pound from what they should merit.

There have been a number of stabilized crossbreeds using Brahmas where the cross itself has been upbred for potency and beef qualities.

---

[13]*Idem.*

[14]*Idem.*

These undoubtedly will eventually dominate the southern U. S. and the Caribbean.

The Santa Gertrudis was developed by the King Ranch and is a Brahma-Shorthorn cross. The Brangus is Brahma-Angus. The Braeford is a Brahma-Hereford. The Beefmaster is Brahma, Hereford and Shorthorn. The Charbray is a cross between the Brahma and the French Charolais. The latter is a dual purpose dairy animal in France and is large like the Holstein.

It is almost impossible to make a comparative analysis between breeds. The advocates of each breed have almost a religious fanaticism on the subject of their favorite. When someone has spent 25 years developing a fine herd of a particular breed, he develops a blind spot about any favorable qualities on another breed.

The universities and government agencies are afraid to touch the subject because of the partisan outcries that would come from their friends and supporters on the publication of any unfavorable comparisons. Reports on weaning weights and calf crop percentages from individual herds are totally unreliable when one doesn't have constant conditions such as number of head of cows per bull, whether or not calves were given supplementary feed, etc. On this particular subject, so-called "impeccable sources" have to be checked. On one particular breed the president of a major stockyards company is widely quoted as an impartial source. He personally happens to own a show herd of this particular breed.

Here are a few statistics:

LEADING STATES IN THE PRODUCTION OF VARIOUS BREEDS OF PUREBRED CATTLE[15]

States in Which Largest Number of Calves Were Registered in 1956

Rank	*Angus*	*Brahman*	*Hereford*	*Polled Hereford*	*Shorthorn and Polled Shorthorn**
1	Missouri	Texas	Texas	Texas	Illinois
2	Iowa	Florida	Oklahoma	Missouri	Iowa
3	Illinois	Louisiana	Kansas	Illinois	Indiana
4	Texas	California	Nebraska	Mississippi	Missouri
5	Kansas	Arkansas	Montana	Oklahoma	Ohio
6	Kentucky	Alabama	Missouri	Kansas	Kansas
7	Oklahoma	Georgia	Illinois	Georgia	Nebraska
8	Virginia	Arizona	South Dakota	Tennessee	North Dakota
9	Indiana	North Carolina	Colorado	Arkansas	Kentucky
10	Ohio	Mississippi	California	Indiana	South Dakota

*Sept. 1, 1956, to Sept. 1, 1957.

[15]*Beef Cattle* by Snapp and Neumann, 5th Edition, p. 21.

TOTAL NUMBER OF NEW REGISTRATIONS OF PUREBRED BEEF CATTLE–1955[16]

Aberdeen Angus	186,316	
Hereford	522,639	
Polled Hereford	101,084	
Shorthorn (1952)	80,487	(Includes milking shorthorns)
Brahman	16,564	

Here are some of my own personal observations combined with various unscientific rumors, gossip and hearsay. I want to qualify myself. My father had a herd of registered horned Herefords. The company of which I am the head runs horned Herefords, Polled Herefords, Angus and Brangus in 14 states.

1. In average purebred herds of 100 in number, there would be substantially more difference between individuals than between the average of one breed and another.
2. On a side of beef hanging in a locker, no expert in the world could tell whether it came from an Angus, Hereford, or Shorthorn.
3. In 1959-60, Angus calves were bringing 1c/lb. more from feeders than Herefords of the same quality.
4. Hereford bulls are slightly better breeders than Angus in the range areas and you don't need as high a ratio to get the same calf crop.
5. Brahmas are wilder and harder to handle. You need better fences.
6. Herefords do not need as much care in blizzards and seem to travel best.
7. Angus rarely get cancer eye.
8. Angus have less trouble calving as first calf heifers.
9. Brahmas and Brahma crosses are bigger in weight for age but they don't grade out as well as the pure British breeds. For example, it is almost impossible to feed them up to prime no matter how long you have them on corn.
10. In purchasing feeders from a central market where you want to avoid any mixture of dairy blood, your best bet is Herefords because any extraneous element shows up on the color usually. This is not true of Angus where the black is dominant. In the Ozarks and Florida the so-called "Southern Black" is often part Jersey, part Angus, and part "miscellaneous."
11. There is a definite advantage to sticking with the breed most

[16]*Encyclopaedia Britannica*, Volume 5, 1958, p. 47.

popular in your particular area for the following reasons:

a. You have a wider selection in getting herd replacements.

b. Buyers come to the area where the breed of their preference is most widespread.

c. Markets and auctions will favor the breed most common to the area.

d. Bulls will always cross fences and you will have less cross-bred calves if you have the same breed as your neighbor.

e. In areas of the west where you and your neighbors share common government grazing permits, you will make yourself unpopular in a hurry if you try to pioneer with a new breed of bull.

Chapter VII

The Big Spreads

This chapter is going to be a thumbnail historical sketch of the big cattle empires which rose and fell on our western range. We are not going to try to cover all of them and we will limit ourselves to those which have at one time or another directly or indirectly operated over tracts of ground in excess of 600,000 acres.

Because of the almost complete impossibility of ever assembling this size tract from groups of small holdings once the land has been split up into little farms and ranches, you will find that almost all of the big spreads originated early in the 1800's or just after the Civil War and usually before or just after the territory became a state.

The general pattern involves a strong character with capital acquired by inheritance or from some other enterprise moving into an area which consists largely of open range, government lands, and Indian territory. He proceeded to acquire choice tracts of land around the water holes and established his headquarters. In some areas he acquired the watered districts by recorded deed; in other areas he held them by force-of-arms. His cattle ranged in common with other large ranches as far as they could graze from water. The amount of land they occupied was generally limited only by the amount of capital he had available to buy cattle and hire gunmen.

Naturally, when the range was unlimited and the only competition for grass was with wild game, there was no problem except for Indian forays. However, when the cattle population expanded sufficiently that a drouth put a squeeze on pasture, then the strong survived and the weak went under. As things became more civilized, various states, territories and districts developed a law of "customary range." This was a mutual agreement among the ranchers that apart from the deeded homesteads and water holes that the use of certain general areas of range land belonged to the person who got there first and who had been grazing it for a number of years. This was not usually limited to a single person but to groups of five or six ranchers in the general area and their immediate relatives. Boundaries of "customary range" were usually large rivers, generally insurmountable mountain crests, and other natural obstacles that cattle would not usually cross.

After the Civil War, fences and barbed wire came into common use and land rights were more clearly delineated. Formal title was taken from the government in many areas with regular deeds being recorded.

About this time in the more settled and congested areas it became customary to record water rights. On given streams the men who first recorded had certain priorities and various use rights which could not be infringed by late comers even if they moved upstream to the original settler.

In the very complex system of laws and customs that developed, range rights, range leases, and water rights could be bought and sold as well as deeded land. Most of the "big spreads" that existed in the late 19th Century and continued on into the early 20th Century or are still in existence, have possibly 30% or 40% deeded land, controlling all of the water and good meadows. This land is "checkerboarded" with the various tracts of federal or state grazing land controlled by lease permits from one or another bureau of the government or state involved.

"In 1906, Theodore Roosevelt enlarged the forest reserves and began the active policy of conserving, improving and enlarging the public lands. Now 405,595,899 acres are federally owned in the eleven "Public Lands" states of the West. The proportion controlled by the government varies from 35% in Montana to 87% in Nevada with an average of 54% for all eleven.

Supervision of this mighty slice of America is divided among the Departments of the Interior, National Defense, and Agriculture with eight major bureaus (National Forests, Grazing Districts, Indian Reservations, National Parks, Soil Conservation, Navy, Army, Fish and Wildlife) handling the actual administration through even more numerous subdivisions."[1]

Generally speaking, anyone who was strong enough and capable enough to assemble and hold a tract of American land in excess of 400,000 acres had a dramatic impact on the history of his State and in many cases moved on to the national scene, either financially or politically.

We shall start off with the King Ranch which is probably the most famous although it is not the largest as often believed. Also it is not typical of most of the "big spreads" for the following reasons:

1. It was mostly on deeded land.
2. It started over 100 years ago and is still going strong.

[1]*Cowboys and Cattle Kings,* Sonnichsen, University of Oklahoma Press, 1950, p. 223.

3. The original King, Kennedy, and Kleberg families have consistently produced leaders every generation and have stayed firmly in control.
4. From the very beginning members of the family have not only been pioneers in ranch administration but all have been of a scientific bent and have been one of the most constructive forces within the entire industry.

THE KING RANCH

Richard King was born July 10, 1824 in New York City of Irish immigrant parents. Almost nothing further is known of his background or lineage. At the age of 11, after being apprenticed to a jeweler, he ran away to sea as a stowaway and subsequent cabin boy on the Desdemona. Over the next ten years he worked himself up to be a pilot and subsequently a captain on the riverboats that plied the coastal ports and rivers along the Gulf of Mexico.

In 1843 he started a long association with another riverboat captain named Mifflin Kennedy who came from a devout Quaker family in Chester County, Pennsylvania. During the period 1846 to 1848 both King and Kennedy were instrumental in supplying the forces of Zachary Taylor along the Rio Grande and subsequent operations into Matamoros and Monterrey.

On March 1, 1850 the firm of M. Kennedy & Company of Brownsville, Texas was organized with four equal partners: King, Kennedy, Charles Stillman, and James O'Donnell. Within a few years this firm had almost a complete monopoly of all trade along the Rio Grande and to all the ports of Northeastern Mexico. It was estimated that the firm consistently averaged out a profit of $40,000 per year on an original capital investment of $80,000. Besides that, the partners participated individually in joint ventures with others on speculations with the cargoes.[2] There is no question but that the purchasing power of the dollar was ten times during that period what it is today so this became one of the principal businesses of the area.

In 1852, Kennedy married Petra Vela de Vidal, the 26 year old widow of a colonel in the Mexican Army, and the mother of five. The bridegroom accepted the faith of his Catholic bride. The bride came from a major landowning family with connections all along the border. Both King and Kennedy spoke Spanish and had numerous close friends with the top land grant families in both Mexico and Texas. This may have been one of the explanations of their phenomenal success in both trade and their later land purchase programs.

---

[2]*The King Ranch*, Tom Lea, Little, Brown & Co., 1957, Vol. I, pp. 1-94.

In 1852, King became interested in land speculation and with a party rode into an area 125 miles north of the Rio Grande near the Santa Gertrudis Creek. He later said to Kennedy, "Land and Livestock have a way of increasing in value. Cattle and horses, sheep and goats, will reproduce themselves into value. But boats—they have a way of wrecking, decaying, falling apart, decreasing in value, and increasing in cost of operation."[3]

In February of 1852 an act of the Texas Legislature had confirmed the ownership of original Spanish and Mexican land grants to rightful heirs and succeeding purchasers. However, the owners had all been driven off by Indians, mustangers (gatherers of wild horses), and assorted border outlaws. King set himself to start purchasing these lands from the heirs and owners who had been driven off and who considered them to be economically worthless without an army of guns to hold them.

His initial purchase was the 15,500 acres of the Rincon de Santa Gertrudis from the widow and heirs of Juan Mendiola on July 25, 1853 for the sum of $300, coming to about 2c per acre.[4] At this time he was a partner with Legs Lewis, a captain in the Texas Rangers, who was able to furnish military support to hold this and subsequent acquisitions. The two built a fortified camp on the Santa Gertrudis which was the beginning of the ranching industry between the Nueces and the Rio Grande.

The drought conditions of 1854 and 1855 enabled King and Lewis to pick up cattle at $5 per head to stock the ranch. To all ranch operations King applied his detailed and meticulous bookkeeping and records that he had used in the steamboat business. Shortly afterwards King's steamboat partner Kennedy started buying lands in the area.

In December of 1854 King married Henrietta Chamberlain, the daughter of a Presbyterian minister from New England. Her father had founded one of the first Protestant churches in the Rio Grande area.

In December of 1860 the firm of R. King & Company was formed for the pooling of all land and livestock interests. King had a three-eighths interest, Kennedy a three-eighths interest, and James Walworth two-eighths. Walworth was another steamboat skipper who had worked for M. Kennedy & Company.

During the war M. Kennedy & Company put many of their boats under Mexican Registry and made huge profits smuggling cotton and

[3]*Idem*, p. 100.
[4]*Idem*, p. 105-110.

supplies through the Union blockade. Substantial amounts of King beef went to New Orleans for the Confederacy. After Brownsville was captured by Union troops, King fled his ranch one jump ahead of a Federal cavalry patrol. While the Civil War caused considerable loss, their trading profits, stuck in gold in Matamoros, salvaged both the ranch and the shipping companies after the war.

In 1866 partner Charles Stillman withdrew from the shipping company and retired to New York. There his money from the border developed the National City Bank of New York. Walworth died and King and Kennedy bought his interest from the estate for $50,000. In 1867 and 1868, King and Kennedy divided their holdings and started the stupendous job of fencing with heavy posts and three planks. Barbed wire didn't come in till 1874. With the division King started using the new brand, the Running W. By 1870, they had liquidated most of the shipping company and were putting their full time in ranching.

With the Texas Rangers prohibited by order of the Reconstruction regime, the next ten years were devoted to repelling marauders from across the border. Texas ranchmen estimated that about 200,000 head were being stolen annually. In 1870, The Stock Raisers Association of Western Texas was formed with Mifflin Kennedy as President. In 1874, the Texas Rangers were reconstituted and, under their famous Captain L. H. McNelly, the situation was rapidly brought under control. King, however, had managed to hold his own with his armed retainers, fortified relay stations, and a shotgun loaded with buckshot which he carried instead of the traditional six shooter. Both McNelly and King had their paid informers across the border. As much by this as any other means they were able to be at the right place at the right time.

On June 12, 1875, the Ranger captain caught 12 bandits on the Palo Alto prairie and dumped their bodies in the main square of Brownsville for relatives to identify and claim. The advent of the telegraph line and the ability to alert and assemble both the Rangers and the U. S. Army broke the back of the rustler movement.

Richard King's motto was: "Buy land and never sell." He ultimately acquired title to more than 600,000 acres. "Every land acquisition King ever made was done through lawyers. They transacted the business. They advised King when he had rights to possession. King bought every piece of land he came to own. He sometimes bought one piece again and again to satisfy multiple claimants."[5]

---

[5]*Idem*, p. 300.

Richard King died in 1885. Under the management of his widow and Robert Kleberg, Sr., his son-in-law, the ranch was increased to over 1,200,000 acres. At the death of Mrs. King in 1925, her will provided for some division of the property ten years after her death. However, some parts of it were put back together again. The present King Ranch Corporation has about 735,000 acres.[6]

Aside from their ranch acquisitions and operations, the King, Kennedy and Kleberg families had an astonishing record as experimenters and innovators:

1. They developed the Santa Gertrudis breed, a stabilized cross between the Shorthorn and the Brahma, for tropical countries which has become one of the principal breeds of the southern U.S. and Latin America.
2. They were one of the principal developers and popularizers of the Quarter Horse, and the King Ranch Quarter Horses have become so famous as to almost be considered a separate sub-breed.
3. They did not oppose the advent of settlers but encouraged them and practically founded and developed the town of Kingsville with the Kleberg Town and Improvement Company.
4. In conjunction with the Bureau of Animal Husbandry and with experiments actually conducted at the ranch, Robert Kleberg was one of the principal leaders in the study and elimination of Texas Cattle Tick Fever. He sponsored the organization of the Texas Livestock Sanitary Commission and was its first head.
5. Robert J. Kleberg, Jr. has been one of the Southwest's leaders in scientific brush eradication and has personally invented much of the equipment generally used.
6. They have currently expanded their integrated operations into Pennsylvania, Australia, Cuba, and Brazil.

THE BAY STATE LAND AND CATTLE COMPANY

This company was started in the 1870's with Massachusetts and Maine capital in addition to Scottish and English money. Its founders started in western Nebraska with the Half Circle Block. By the spring of 1883, they were expanding fast and bought out the Circle Arrow Ranch for $700,000. The next year they bought out "Coad's Kingdom" stretching from Chimney Rock to Scotts Bluff. In addition, they leased Union Pacific Railroad lands all the way into Wyoming and the Big Horn Basin. Under their new manager, John A. McShane, they built

[6] *The Big Ranch Country*, J. W. Williams, Terry Brothers, 1954, pp. 251-255.

up to a herd of 150,000 head.[7]

Very little of the land was deeded, but by the law of "customary range" enforced by the power of top hired guns and domination of the local state legislatures, they controlled over 3,000,000 acres.

The blizzards of 1886 and 1887 reputedly caused the Bay State a loss of 100,000 head. "The carcasses formed an almost solid covering between Pumpkin Creek and the roughly parallel Wild Cat Mountains; the deep creek bed choked with the dead stock for ten miles. It broke the great power of the Bay State, with all its eastern and British backing, and opened a vast new region to settlers, and to rival cattle empires."[8]

THE FRENCH-GLENN CATTLE COMPANY

At the age of 23, Pete French left the Sacramento Valley in California May 13, 1872 for southeastern Oregon with 1,200 two-year-old Shorthorn heifers, 40 bulls, and 50 picked horses. The cattle and a good supply of ready cash were being supplied by his future father-in-law, the famous Dr. Hugh Glenn of the Jacinto Land Grant and at that time the biggest wheat producer in the U.S.

Over a period of a quarter of a century, until he was shot by a settler he was trying to drive out, he amassed control of over a million acres on a 60,000 head operation running along the Blitzen Valley east of the Steens Mountains. His operation differs from many of the others in that he moved into an area of existing operations and had to assemble his position by purchase and maneuver as well as the customary force. While there were fertile river valleys which permitted the operation of small farms, he had the advantage in this later period of being almost 300 miles from the nearest railhead at Winnemucca, Nevada over very difficult terrain. This put smaller ranchers who did not have the proper staff for a big trail drive at an economic disadvantage.

The growth of his empire was accomplished by both traditional and novel means:

1. He had a large and constant supply of gold and cash through his family connections and his own astute business dealings, to use to buy out his neighbors on various fluctuations of the cattle cycle.
2. He initially purchased strategic tracts of government land at $1 per acre with federal scrip that he had bought at a discount.

[7]*The Cattlemen,* Mari Sandoz, Hastings House, 1958, p. 241.
[8]*Idem,* p. 261.

3. He used his purchases in strung out 40 acre strips to tie up the perimeter of each of his ranches on natural mountain boundaries which he immediately blocked with fences along the gaps.
4. He was one of the first men in Oregon to use a surveyor and record deeded water rights for irrigating his low meadows and effectively squeezing out any new settlers.

The following conversations from Elizabeth Lambert Wood's excellent fictionalized biography, "Pete French, Cattle King" may not have taken place but they are typical of the period:

> "Pete," added Rye, his voice again slow and deliberate, "in time you'll change your mind. You'll grow to have a better understanding of events taking place in Harney Valley. The old days of free land and free everything are gone forever. Let's both bless today and let the old times go. The little fellows have come in. There's land enough for all."
>
> "Rye, you know I won't do any of them any harm if they will let me alone. Most of them settled around the edge of P Ranch to fatten off my cattle. They don't call it rustling but they live off me."
>
> "Take it easy, Pete. Why don't you let them do it?"
>
> "Let them do it! Do you know that I tried hiring some and caught them putting their own brands on my calves while I was paying them wages?"[9]
>
> . . . .
>
> Oliver turned white, and, clearly frightened, coughed and sputtered, "I'll have the law on you Pete French. I'm holding out to get this pasture. . . . The land hasn't been surveyed. My rights are just as good as yours, and maybe a whole lot better."
>
> "The only difference," Pete answered, "is that I happened to get here first. Oliver, let me buy you out lock, stock and barrel. I'll pay you a good price, bigger than anyone else will offer."[10]

After Pete French was shot, the empire gradually disintegrated. Part was acquired by Handley's Double O to the north and part by the Swift Packing Company. Subsequently the federal government took over most of the valley for one of our major wildlife sanctuaries.[11]

THE XIT

This ranch is unique in that it was assembled entirely out of deeded land and more or less at one fell swoop rather than over a period of generations like the King Ranch. In 1882 the State of Texas had set aside approximately 3,500,000 acres of land west of the Panhandle to be deeded to the firm that would build a new capitol at Austin. The

---

[9]*Pete French, Cattle King,* Elizabeth Lambert Wood, Binfords and Mort, 1951, p. 207.
[10]*Idem,* p. 215.
[11]*Idem,* p. 229.

contract was awarded to Taylor, Babcock, and Company of Chicago. The deeds were to be accomplished at the completion of the capitol building which was estimated to cost $3,000,000.

To develop, fence, and stock the property, they formed the Capitol Freehold Land and Investment Company, Limited, with principally British capital and acquired $15,000,000. The English officials included such men as the Earl of Aberdeen and the Marquis of Tweeddale, a Scotch banker, who was Chairman of the Board.

B. H. Campbell, the first manager, was one of the first to make extensive use of the new barbed wire and constructed almost 750 miles of fence. Campbell was one of the original founders of the American Shorthorn Breeders' Association and constantly brought in a top quality of Shorthorn and Hereford bulls. By the fall of 1887 the herds totaled nearly 120,000.

A general dissatisfaction of the British stockholders with the operating profits caused them to have Campbell fired, and Abner Taylor and A. G. Boyce were put in charge in 1888.

Early in 1890 Boyce leased 2,000,000 acres between the Yellowstone and the Missouri rivers in Montana—bringing the XIT range to 5,000,000, the giant of them all.[12]

By 1901 the XIT began to sell off its land. By 1906, 2,000,000 acres had been sold. Some of the sales were to the Matador Land and Cattle Company of Dundee, Scotland which now began to move up to first place in Texas.

SWAN LAND AND CATTLE COMPANY, LIMITED

The original assemblage was made by Alexander Hamilton Swan who also formed the Wyoming Hereford Association which was probably historically the most important single entity in importing Herefords and popularizing the breed through the range country. From 1921 on to the present day it has been operating as the Wyoming Hereford Ranch.[13]

A Scotch group formed the Swan Land and Cattle Company, Limited in 1883 and bought out the Swan holdings in Wyoming and Nebraska. The land claimed was centered on the Laramie River, a range 130 miles long east and west, and from 42 to 100 miles north and south, mostly public domain. The next year the company bought railroad lands, which were checkerboarded in alternate sections with the public domain and open only to regular settler entry.[14]

---

[12] *The Cattlemen*, Mari Sandoz, Hastings House, 1958, pp. 296-325.

[13] *The Hereford in America*, Ornduff, p. 53.

[14] *The Cattlemen*, Mari Sandoz, Hastings House, 1958, p. 247.

John Clay, a Scotsman who had been put in charge by the overseas interest, was the principal leader of the Wyoming Stock Growers Association which completely dominated the legislature and political officials of Wyoming for many years and extended its influence into Colorado, Nebraska, and even to the Capitol in Washington.

They were able to prevent any round-up being held by anyone without a foreman appointed by the Association to conduct it. No brands were recognized but those of the big ranchers. In addition, a $3,000 bond was required to be posted which eliminated any small rancher. They brought in hired gunmen as range detectives and kept inspectors at all stockyards and railheads.

"There was no denying that the British cattle interests and their employees were determined to have the Wyoming range regulated and orderly. Perhaps they looked upon the American public domain as something like their own early backlands, to be gifted by the king to his favorites or appropriated by any aggressive chieftain with the long bows to hold it." [15]

The blizzards of '86 and the subsequent collapse of the cattle market rocked the Swan holdings badly and they were forced to give up part of their empire. The steady influx of settlers and their votes put in sheriffs and legislators hostile to the big cattle companies and their political power was broken. When President Cleveland threatened to call out the cavalry to remove cattle from the Indian lands and forced the removal of 130 miles of Swan fencing on the public lands, it was the beginning of the end.

The final breakup of the big empires on the public domain came with the advent of Theodore Roosevelt and his appointment of the famous Confederate Cavalry leader, Colonel Mosby, as his range inspector. In June 1904, the Kinkaid Act went into effect permitting every bona fide homesteader to take up to 640 acres of land. If the settler had received a 160-acre homestead in the past, he could enter 480 now, the new homestead requiring five year residence and $800 in improvements.[16]

The large cattlemen tried to take advantage of this with false filings from eastern pensioners, whose names they used, and numerous other devices. The President cracked down and in the "Roosevelt Roundup" dozens of the large ranchers were hauled into court. When most were acquitted or fined lightly Roosevelt brought in the Secret Service to protect surveyors, fired a U.S. Marshal, and cleaned house on the

[15] *Idem*, p. 335.
[16] *Idem*, p. 447.

local judiciary. In 1911 Bartlett Richards, the brother of a Governor of Wyoming, whose holdings in Nebraska and Wyoming were second only to the former Swan empire, was sent to prison, where he died. An era had come to an end.[17]

THE MATADOR

About 1879, H. H. Campbell in conjunction with A. M. Brittain, a Fort Worth banker, began to assemble land around Ballard Springs, Texas and gave their company the name of Matador. In 1883, A. M. Brittain went abroad and joined forces with some Scotch financiers from Dundee, Scotland and raised $1,250,000 for expansion. In 1891, Campbell resigned to go into business for himself, but when he quit they were branding 20,000 calves per year.

In 1902, the Matador Land and Cattle Company bought another 200,000 acres in Oldham County along the Canadian River west of Amarillo. This was purchased from the XIT, which was now starting to liquidate. In 1904, they secured a government lease of 500,000 acres on the Cheyenne Reservation in South Dakota. They also picked up another lease along the Saskatchewan River in Canada. By 1906 they were well above 1,000,000 acres in controlled land. In 1913, they picked up another 550,000 acre lease on the Belknap Indian Reservation near Harlem, Montana.

Back in Texas they continued to assemble deeded land and shortly were close to the 1,000,000 acre mark with possibly an equal amount of lease and controlled range in other sections, making a total of 2,000,000 acres.

In 1891, A. J. Lingertwood became local manager and Murdo MacKenzie, superintendent. Following Lingertwood, J. M. Jackson was manager from 1909 until 1924. In later years, M. J. Reilly was manager until his death in 1946.[18]

The famous "V" of the Matador brand became associated with possibly the most outstanding group of Hereford commercial breeding stock in the country. Generally the brand alone was worth a 2c per pound premium at all of the big auctions and stockyards. Murdo MacKenzie, for a number of years, bought carloads of the top registered bulls from the internationally known Robert H. Hazlett herds of El Dorado, Kansas. "In 1931 and again in 1935, the Matador company bought the top-price bull of the National Western sale at Denver, the latter being also the champion bull of the show there."[19]

---

[17]*Idem*, p. 448-455.

[18]*The Big Ranch Country*, J. W. Williams, 1954, pp. 120-125, pp. 216-218.

[19]*The Hereford in America*, Ornduff, 1957, p. 144.

In 1951, the famous Lazard Freres & Co. of 44 Wall Street bought out the company and put Mr. Albert K. Mitchell in charge. He had formerly been twice president of the American Hereford Association and was one of the top cattlemen in the U.S. Over the course of the next nine years, lands and cattle were sold off, principally to smaller ranchers on the fringe of this vast empire. A major portion of the female breeding stock was purchased by syndicates headed by Mr. Buster Wheat of Allen, Kansas and Oppenheimer Industries, Inc., Kansas City, Missouri.

THE WAGGONER ESTATE

This included 510,000 acres south of Vernon, Texas and, until recently, 176,000 acres east of Las Vegas, New Mexico. By including oil rights, this might be the most valuable ranch holding in the U.S.

Dan Waggoner was in northwestern Wichita County as early as 1879 and on the lower Pease by 1881. He had a grass lease on the Kiowa-Comanche Reservation in Oklahoma of around 500,000 acres that was put under fence and held past 1900.

The famous Indian Chief, Quanah Parker, was actually employed by Waggoner as an extra ranch hand. During this period his famous 3-D brand shared the Indian ranges with Burnett's Four Sixes, and Sugg's O H Triangle.

Where he differed from his neighbors and other lease operators was that he saw the coming end of the open range and started to assemble deeded lands by purchase from 1900 on.[20]

One famous story of the early range was the time a rustler stole 144 steers of Waggoner's and put a Box around the 3-D with a bar iron. "No Box 3-D was registered so Dan recorded the new brand in his own name and went to reclaim the steers from the brand burner, with the weight of the guns on his side, of course." [21]

As an example of how the owners and managers of the Big Spreads have moved on to the national scene is the case of the manager of the Waggoner Estate from 1941 to 1953, Mr. R. B. Anderson. He was first Deputy Secretary of Defense and was Secretary of the Treasury in President Eisenhower's Cabinet.

THE FOUR SIXES

Burk Burnett started operating on government leases east of the Waggoners at about the same time. By 1905, he was forced out and

[20] *The Big Ranch Country*, Williams, 1954, pp. 139-141.
[21] *The Cattlemen*, Sandoz, 1958, p. 221.

R. L. Duke, a foreman on the XIT Ranch in 1895. (Courtesy, Rita Blanca Studio, Dalhart, Texas)

A "remuda" of the XIT in the 19th century. (Courtesy, Rita Blanca Studio, Dalhart, Texas)

When President Roosevelt appointed Colonel Mosby, the famous Confederate raider, to straighten out the range barons, there was no more shooting of government surveyors. (Courtesy, Library of Congress)

Matador cowboys getting a cow out of a bog in the Canadian River near Tascosa, Texas, around 1890. (Courtesy, Rita Blanca Studio, Dalhart, Texas)

Albert K. Mitchell, manager of the Matador for Lazard Freres and former president of the American Hereford Association. (Courtesy, American Hereford Assn.)

moved to King County, 125 miles southwest of Wichita Falls, and Carson County, 30 miles northeast of Amarillo. His son, Tom Burnett, started his own Triangle Brand and began assembling his own deeded lands. In 1918, the oil boom hit the area and both groups of lands were on their way to becoming very valuable.

One of the interesting features of this family was the rigid will of Burk Burnett, who died in 1922, which will keep the over $6,000,000 estate intact until the death of his granddaughter, Anne. This could preserve the oil-heavy ranch into the next century and be one of the great fortunes of the country.[22]

The present holdings of the Burnett estate and family are about 450,000 acres.

GRANVILLE STUART

Stuart was a Virginian of Scotch descent and may have been the first to start in the beef business in Montana. In 1860, he started fattening lame oxen from settlers on the Oregon Trail in Idaho Territory and sold them as food to the mining camps. In 1866, Nelson Story drove in the first group of 600 Texas longhorns from the Bozeman Trail. By 1880, range overcrowding already existed in western Montana and Granville Stuart brought the first herd over the divide into central Montana. This area became one of the great open range sections of the country. Stuart had married an Indian girl and was still able to maintain his range rights even after the government started to kick off the other white ranchers.

The shift in the period 1880 to 1883 was phenomenal. In a three year period the country shifted from vast herds of buffalo and no cattle to no buffalo and over 600,000 head of cattle. "The great herds on this last stand of the open range grazed upon millions of acres to which the herds' owners had no right other than the fact that they got there first, a 'squatter's right' which was given recognition of sorts in 1877 in the curious law of 'customary range.' In many instances, owners of 30,000 or 40,000 head of cattle owned not one square foot of the land they used, nor even the land upon which their ranch buildings stood." [23]

The branding of "mavericks" became an extremely profitable business. To quote Stuart himself, "Near our home ranch we discovered one rancher whose cows invariably had twin calves and frequently triplets, while the range cows in that vicinity were nearly all barren

[22]*The Big Ranch Country*, Williams, 1954, pp. 202-206.

[23]*Montana: High, Wide, and Handsome*, J. K. Howard, Yale University Press, 1959, pp. 107, 108.

and would persist in hanging around this man's corral, envying his cows, their numerous children and bawling and lamenting their own childless state. This state of affairs continued until we were obliged to call around that way and threaten to hang the man if his cows had any more twins."[24]

COLONEL GOODNIGHT

In 1856, at the age of 20, Charlie Goodnight formed a partnership with his stepbrother, Wes Sheek, to run cattle in Palo Pinto County, in the Comanche country. The next ten years were spent alternating in service with the Rangers and constant skirmishes with the Indians.

In 1866, in company with Oliver Loving, he started a major drive into New Mexico. For the next few years the two men pioneered constant trail drives to Fort Sumner, Denver, and Santa Fe and made a considerable fortune, mostly on government contract sales. After Loving died from wounds in an Indian raid, Goodnight established the first major ranch in southern Colorado near the Apishapa River in 1867.[25]

In 1876, after having formed a partnership with the Irish nobleman, John Adair, they moved from their headquarters at Trinidad, Colorado into the Palo Duro Canyon of the Texas Panhandle. This was the beginning of the famous JA brand taken from the initials of John Adair. At its height, in both deeded and leased land, the partnership controlled over 1,300,000 acres. On Adair's death the range was split up but Mrs. Cornelia Adair, the widow, kept much of her portion intact and the present Cornelia Adair Estate is one of the principal landowners in the country (319,000 acres).[26]

Goodnight was also one of the principal owners of the Interstate Land and Cattle Company which at one time controlled almost 3,000,000 acres of New Mexico public range. Here a major battle ensued with Teddy Roosevelt in his program of making private ranchers remove all their fencing from the public lands. Roosevelt won.[27]

C. C. SLAUGHTER

C. C. Slaughter was the first native cattle king of Texas. His father, who had dealt in early wild Spanish cattle, had been Sam Houston's right hand man and the first man to be married in the Republic, C. C.

---

[24]*Idem.*
[25]*The Cattlemen*, Sandoz, 1958, pp. 83-85.
[26]*The Big Ranch Country*, Williams, 1954, pp. 213-215.
[27]*The Cattlemen*, Sandoz, 1958, p. 443.

being the first child born of the marriage.[28]

He started on his own in the cattle business when he was seventeen years old with $520 he had made by hauling and trading lumber and wheat along the Trinity River. He invested the money in a herd of cattle which he moved 300 miles northwest where he started the Long S Ranch on Dillingham Prairie.[29] Although there is some argument about it, he is supposed to have trailed the first Texas herd into Abilene and shipped it out by rail.

He shortly went into banking and became president of the First National Bank at Dallas. By 1879, he was supposed to have made over $1,500,000 from cattle and was buying up state lands in Texas almost by the county. In addition, he leased an empire of a ranch in Montana and was trailing steers up there to finish on the hearty northern grasses.[30]

At his height in 1905, he is credited with 100,000 cattle on 1,500,000 acres of both deeded and leased land.[31] Substantial subdivision and sale of the lands continued by the estate until 1937 when the discovery of oil in Hockley County made wealthy the remaining heirs who still held part of the old ranch.[32]

SMS[33] OF STAMFORD, TEXAS

S. M. Swenson came over from Sweden in the early 1830's and made his first trip to Texas in 1838. He became one of the biggest merchants in Austin when the capital was moved there and was a close personal friend of Sam Houston. When the Civil War broke out he wasn't in favor of secession and ran off to New Mexico. He reputedly got most of his assets converted into gold and buried under a chimney in his home. When the war ended, he was established in New York and became an investment banker associated with such men as Frank Vanderlip and Mortimer Schiff. In 1888 he brought back his nephew A. J. Swenson from Sweden, whose family has been managing the ranch ever since.

However, the ranch does not belong to them but is the property of the corporation started by S. M. Swenson before he left Texas. "He

---

[28]*Idem,* p. 58.

[29]*Great Roundup,* L. Nordyke, William Morrow & Co., 1955, p. 19.

[30]*The Cattlemen,* Sandoz, 1958, pp. 238, 239.

[31]*Idem,* p. 120.

[32]*The Big Ranch Country,* 1954, p. 230.

[33]*Cowboys and Cattle Kings,* Sonnichsen, University of Oklahoma Press, 1950, p. 141.

bought scrip covering railroad lands, purchased additional land and eventually had three enormous blocks of real estate he called the Ellerslie, Flat Top, and Throckmorton Ranches."[34]

In 1906, they organized a corporation which bought the huge Spur Ranch on the plains at the base of the Texas Panhandle. The stockholders were Vanderlip, Schiff, Emery and Swenson. Emery owned three-fifths of the stock. The group developed a town in the middle of their holdings and sold off thousands of acres of farm land between 1910 and 1915. They combined the sturdy traditions of the Old West with the grim business methods of Wall Street.

About the time World War II began, the corporation was dissolved. The owners divided the property and the Swenson Land and Cattle Company bought all but Emery's share. The Emery heirs wanted $5 an acre, but old E. P. Swenson wouldn't pay it. He said he would not give money like that for land he was used to getting for $2 an acre. Now that same land is going for as high as $20 but nobody anticipated the land boom that followed the war and the Emery holdings were allowed to remain in the possession of the heirs. AJ's son, Eric Swenson, is now in charge of the Emery acreage. Although the grouped holdings are probably less than one-third of what they were at the zenith, they still involve over 300,000 acres. The "SMS" brand is still known as one of the outstanding "name" brands in the country.

RAILROAD AND UNIVERSITY LANDS

During the 19th Century when the railroads were crossing the country, both the Federal Government and the States deeded them public lands as compensation to encourage their more rapid construction. The Federal Government characteristically gave them alternate sections on either side of the right-of-way. Texas had a deal with Jay Gould's Texas and Pacific to give them 16 to 20 sections for every mile of construction. Gould put in 900 miles but the State did not have the necessary 12,000,000 acres of public land left and settled with 5,000,000 acres which was the greatest quantity ever transferred to a single private establishment.

This generally ran across West Texas in the vicinity of Midland and Odessa. Most of this was disbursed but Fraser, Burr and McAlpin acquired a good portion of it and the firm still owns 1,700,000 acres and is the largest private landowner in the state of Texas. They do not operate it as a ranch but lease it to others.[35]

---

[34] *Idem*, p. 143.

[35] *The Big Ranch Country*, Williams, 1954, pp. 230-232.

The University of Texas owns over 2,000,000 acres granted by the state near the Pecos River which has considerable oil revenue. They lease to private ranchers at substantially less than market rents and with many of the characteristics of the old Taylor right leases.

The Union Pacific has retained tremendous land holdings which make up sections of some of the finest ranches in the country. The St. Louis-San Francisco Railway Company has large holdings, including 50% of the stock of the New Mexico and Arizona Land Company, which at one time had over 750,000 acres of deeded lands with most of the minerals intact.

NEW MEXICO AND ARIZONA LAND COMPANY

The stock for this company is traded on the American Stock Exchange. There are 1,000,000 shares authorized, issued and outstanding, of which, as just mentioned, over 50% are controlled by the St. Louis-San Francisco Railway Company in St. Louis. The headquarters of both companies are in St. Louis.

As an example of a non-operating company engaged principally in the leasing of southwestern land, we are going to reproduce in its entirety the financial statement published in its annual report for the year ending December 31, 1959.

COMPARATIVE STATEMENT OF INCOME AND RETAINED INCOME

	Year Ended December 31	
	1959	*1958**
INCOME:		
Rents-grazing leases	$ 115,195	$ 116,118
Rents-uranium leases	145,355	...
Rents-oil and gas leases	95,196	102,998
Gravel royalties	200	25,486
Profit on land sale contracts	84,168	70,260
Interest and dividends	61,117	52,865
Miscellaneous	3,914	2,408
	$ 505,145	$ 370,135
EXPENSE:		
Salaries and administrative expenses	$ 21,581	$ 26,513
Taxes, other than taxes on income	21,495	22,305
Amortization of premiums on securities	6,273	4,029
	$ 49,349	$ 52,847
Net income before income taxes	$ 455,796	$ 317,288
Estimated income taxes	168,813	160,197
Net income	$ 286,983	$ 157,091
Retained income at beginning of year	1,512,159	1,355,068
Retained income at end of year	$1,799,142	$1,512,159

*Restated.

COMPARATIVE BALANCE SHEET

ASSETS

	December 31	
	1959	1958
Current Assets:		
Cash	$ 237,048	$ 308,534
Accrued interest and other receivables	24,630	27,994
	$ 261,678	$ 336,528
Securities, at cost—which approximates market:		
Common stocks—Utilities	$ 268,373	$ ——
Bonds		
U. S. Government	285,199	385,407
State, County and Municipal	1,617,918	1,422,260
	$2,171,490	$1,807,667
Properties, at cost or less:		
Land	$ 540,092	$ 540,288
Mineral rights in land sold	36,462	36,462
Automobile, less reserve for depreciation	1,623	2,087
	$ 578,177	$ 578,837
Other Assets:		
Receivables under land sale contracts	$ 159,997	$ 264,200
	$3,171,342	$2,987,232

LIABILITIES AND SHAREHOLDERS' EQUITY

	1959	1958
Current Liabilities:		
Accounts payable	$ 2,905	$ 4,634
Estimated federal and state income taxes	144,544	163,000
Other accrued taxes	9,280	9,547
	$ 156,729	$ 177,181
Deferred Credits:		
Rents collected in advance	$ 97,628	$ 95,685
Unrealized profit on land sale contracts	117,843	202,207
	$ 215,471	$ 297,892
Shareholders' Equity:		
Capital stock, $1 par value—		
Authorized, issued, and outstanding—		
1,000,000 shares	$1,000,000	$1,000,000
Retained income (see income statement)	1,799,142	1,512,159
	$2,799,142	$2,512,159
	$3,171,342	$2,987,232

The landholdings lie generally along U. S. Highway #66 running from Kingman, Arizona to Albuquerque, New Mexico. The principal holdings lie very close to the Arizona-New Mexico border. There are 622,598 acres owned in fee and over 700,000 additional mineral right acres.

The company customarily leases out its lands rather than attempting to physically operate them.

During the 1959-60 period, the stock has wildly fluctuated generally in the range from 9 to 25. This has been caused principally by various rumors relating to oil and uranium possibilities.

Because many of the deeded acres are checkerboarded with state leases, Indian leases, and other land owned in fee by private lessees, the grazing lands of this particular company are an integral part of ranch operations that might total as much as 3,000,000 acres.

KERN COUNTY LAND COMPANY

This is the largest farming, ranching and land owning company in the U. S. today and possibly only one American in 50 has ever heard of it. The stock is traded on the New York Stock Exchange and is a favorite with the old line investment trusts. The assets of the company undoubtedly have a market net worth in excess of $200,000,000. Generally the company is best known for its oil operations.

However, its VVV Ranch around Seligman, Arizona, the Little Boquillas in southern Arizona, and its holdings in two large ranches in New Mexico might make it the principal land owner in both states. Formerly, its holdings in southern Oregon made it the chief operator in that state.

Kern County itself is in California and the headquarters of the company are in San Francisco. It may directly or indirectly control more irrigated farm land in California than any other single entity. (124,000 acres under cultivation in row crops.)[36]

"The company, incorporated in San Francisco in 1890, had its beginnings in the 1870s. It was started by James Ben Ali Haggin and Lloyd Tevis, two businessmen who had been very successful in the West since coming here from Kentucky.

"Among their ventures was the launching of the great Homestake Mine in the Black Hills of South Dakota in 1877, a project in which they were associated with Senator George Hearst.

"Haggin and Tevis foresaw that the railroads would open up the San Joaquin Valley and began to acquire land along the Kern River for cattle ranching. Apparently the first purchase was made in 1873. Parcels in the Carrissa area were acquired in 1874, and the San Emidio Grant—the site of the present San Emidio Ranch in Kern County—was acquired in 1878.

"The Victorio Land and Cattle Company, a KCL subsidiary with

[36]Annual Stockholders Report, 1959, p. 21.

headquarters at Deming, New Mexico, was incorporated by Haggin and Tevis in 1899. It was transferred to the Kern County Land Company by Haggin in 1910 to assure continuity of management. There are two major areas included—the Animas in Grant and Hidalgo counties, and the Armendaris in Sierra and Socorro counties.

"In Arizona, the subsidiary Boquillas Cattle Company operates the VVV Ranch that runs from Seligman north to the Grand Canyon. It was acquired in 1948.

"The so-called Little Boquillas Ranch, now leased to others, is in southern Arizona in Cochise County and includes the old Spanish Grants of San Rafael de Valle and San Juan de los Boquillas y Nogales, and was acquired in the period from 1901 to 1912.

"All the out-of-state ranches are cow-calf ranches. The San Emidio Ranch in Kern County and the Carissa area in San Luis Obispo County, California, are stocker ranches. The company also has its Gosford Feed Yard in Kern County. Sales from Gosford in 1959 totaled 43,300 head."[37]

The following is quoted from Moody's Industrial Manual:

> "In 1957 merged Chewacan Land & Cattle Co., a subsidiary.
>
> "In December 1958 company sold Oregon Ranch and escrow opened covering ZX Ranch in southern Oregon to Sinter & Brown Co. Transaction included 171,000 acres of fee land and related grazing leases totaling over 1,000,000 acres, all ranch equipment, operating inventories, and over 18,000 head of cattle.
>
> "As part of transaction company acquired Santa Rita Ranch, a 6,000 acre cattle property and Alliance Ranch, a 500 acre farm both near Paso Robles, California.
>
> "In 1958 company, with others formed Marin Oak Development Co. a residential development project.
>
> "Company owns and operates agricultural and cattle properties in California. Subsidiaries operate desert ranches for breeding of calves in Arizona, New Mexico and Oregon. Extensive acreage is leased for farming and company also operates canal system for irrigation purposes in Kern County. Land is leased for oil development to the major oil companies operating in California.
>
> "Company and wholly-owned subsidiaries own approximately 1,900,000 acres of land in California, Arizona, New Mexico and Oregon. Also leases or utilizes under permits, substantial additional acreage for cattle grazing."[38]

---

[37]Letter 29 April 1960, Public Relations Dept., Kern County Land Company.
[38]*Moody's Industrial Manual,* 1959, p. 2,900.

CATTLE OPERATIONS[39]

	Inv. Dec. 31—hd.	*No. Sold in Year*	*Sale Price*
1958	48,182	61,413	Not Stated
1957	58,743	54,832	" "
1956	66,078	34,864	" "
1955	74,176	40,173	$7,790,767

In June 1959, by a stock exchange, Kern acquired assets of Walker Manufacturing Company of Wisconsin. The following chart from the published financial statement includes Walker only for the last year. Add "000's" to all figures:

TEN YEAR SUMMARY[40]

FINANCIAL AND PRODUCTION STATISTICS

		Net Earnings		*Cash Dividends*			
	Operating Revenues	*Total*	*Per Share*	*Total*	*Per Share*	*Net Current Assets*	*Net Assets*
1959	$96,815	$16,645	$3.86	$9,712	$2.25	$37,947	$83,534
1958	82,343	13,333	3.09	9,439	2.25	37,913	76,494
1957	73,221	14,165	3.29	9,328	2.25	40,284	70,696
1956	68,209	12,967	3.02	9,240	2.25	37,221	66,639
1955	63,949	12,720	2.97	9,190	2.25	35,318	62,944
1954	54,664	12,494	2.92	9,209	2.25	33,137	59,455
1953	59,210	11,495	2.68	9,239	2.25	30,530	55,716
1952	57,728	12,490	2.93	9,239	2.25	29,296	53,530
1951	55,992	11,993	2.81	9,236	2.25	25,532	49,341
1950	42,891	12,635	2.97	9,266	2.25	23,808	46,629

NOTE: Net earnings for 1958 do not include the special credit of $1,353,000 representing profit, after taxes, on the sale of a large cattle ranch.

"At December 31, 1959, there were authorized 8,000,000 shares of the Company's $2.50 par value capital stock, of which 4,315,565 were outstanding and 23,600 were held as treasury shares. Comparative 1958 figures, restated to reflect shares issued for the subsequent Walker acquisition, were: authorized, 8,000,000; outstanding, 4,316,965; in treasury, 21,700."[41]

"At the close of 1959, Company stock was owned by 16,027 Share Owners residing in every state of the Union and in several foreign countries. Nearly 1,300 new owners were added by the addition of

[39]*Idem.*

[40]Kern County Land Company Annual Report, 1959, p. 10.

[41]*Idem*, p. 9.

Walker Manufacturing Company. Of total Share Owners, 95 per cent are individuals holding over 70 per cent of the Company's outstanding stock. Nearly half of all owners held 100 shares or less."[42]

The present Chairman of the Board is Mr. George G. Montgomery and the President is Dwight M. Cochran.

In the 1959-60 period the stock ranged generally from 48 to 60 and it paid a dividend of $2.25 per share.

---

[42] *Idem.*

Chapter VIII

Absentee Ownership

There are three men involved in the operation of livestock: (1) the man who owns the land, (2) the man who owns the animals, and (3) the man who does the work. In the U. S. today, in any sizeable operation, it would be extremely unusual to find all three personalities merged in a single individual. Variations of the pattern in this country could run from an American cowboy running cattle owned by a British syndicate on lands leased from the University of Texas to a small farmer who rents a widow's 80 acre pasture to supplement his own.

The division between ownership and management of livestock goes back to the dawn of recorded history. For 4,000 years, absentee owners have been trying to work out incentive plans to get the best job done by their managers. Likewise, the managers have worked just as hard to protect their own interests.

Because cattle, sheep, and goats have to be grazed over wide sections of ground, it was early recognized that an owner could not give the same personal inspection and supervision as he could to a farm plot. Consequently, the straight salary or flat fee was unsatisfactory and some profit sharing plan had to be devised to get the top performance out of the distant herdsman.

One of the earliest recorded management contracts is in the Book of Genesis between Jacob and his father-in-law, Laban: "He [Laban] said, 'What shall I give you?' Jacob said, 'You shall not give me anything; if you will do this for me, I will again feed your flock and keep it; Let me pass through all your flock today, removing from it every speckled and spotted sheep and every black lamb, and the spotted and speckled among the goats; and such shall be my wages. So my honesty will answer for me later, when you come to look into my wages with you, everyone that is not speckled and spotted among the goats and black among the lambs, if found with me shall be counted stolen.' Laban said, 'Good! Let it be as you have said.' But that day Laban removed the he-goats that were striped and spotted, and all the she-goats that were speckled and spotted, everyone that had white on it, and every lamb that was black and put them in charge of his sons; and he set a distance of three days journey between himself and Jacob's; and Jacob fed the rest of Laban's flock."[1]

Laban thought he had made an excellent deal with his herd manager. He had not reckoned on the fact that Jacob had Jehovah as his special agricultural consultant. As in millions of such contracts made before and since, and on Jehovah's advice, who had appeared to him in a dream, he took special action to better his position.

"Then Jacob took fresh rods of poplar and almond and plane, and peeled white streaks in them, exposing the white of the rods. He set the rods which he had peeled in front of the flocks and the runnels, that is, the watering troughs, where the flocks came to drink. And since they bred when they came to drink, the flocks bred in front of the rods so the flocks brought forth striped, speckled, and spotted, and Jacob separated the lambs, and set the faces of the flocks toward the striped and all the black in the flock of Laban; and he put his own droves apart, and did not put them with Laban's flock. Whenever the stronger of the flock were breeding, Jacob layed the rods in the runnels before the eyes of the flock that they might breed among the rods, but for the feebler of the flock he did not lay them there; so the feebler were Laban's, and the stronger Jacob's. Thus the man grew exceedingly rich and had large flocks, maidservants, and menservants, and camels and asses."[2]

While this particular operation may not have been genetically sound in modern times, it is a 4,000 year old version of a rather complicated contract between a man who owned the livestock and a man who did the work.

The third element of the equation involving the man who owns the land is a relatively new one. While the private individual ownership of land goes back thousands of years it generally related to an agricultural plot, a vineyard, or a particularly valuable tract of river bottom. Pasture or grazing land was generally the least desirable portion of the area and was very often owned by the tribe or the state as a common entity and often used by individuals of the tribe with or without restrictions on the number of head that they could run on the communal pasture.

As covered in our previous chapter on the "Big Spreads" this situation prevailed over most of the United States down to the last

---

[1]Genesis, Chapter 30, Verses 31-36, *The Holy Bible*, Revised Standard Version, Thomas Nelson & Sons, 1953.

[2]*Idem*, Genesis, Verses 37-43.

century as far as sheep and beef cattle were concerned. Even today, great parts of our western states are still owned by the federal government or the states themselves with certain individuals having revokable permits to use the public lands in common with others.

If anything as complicated as the arrangement between Jacob and Laban could have been worked out 4,000 years ago, one can only guess at the hundreds of variations in managerial contracts that have been used since. The following are just a few in current use between cattle owners and herd managers in the United States today.

For the time being we will assume that the cattle owner also owns the land or has it under control by a primary lease with either the government or civilian landowners. These basic arrangements could be combined in various proportions:

1. The owner pays the manager a flat salary.
2. The owner gives the manager half the calf crop, but the manager furnishes hay, protein, equipment and all outside labor.
3. The owner keeps the heifer calves and the manager gets the steer calves.
4. The owner furnishes everything except labor and permits the manager to run a certain number of his cattle on the owner's land in addition to the owner's herd. All proceeds from the manager's cattle belong to the manager.
5. The owner pays the manager on the basis of a weight-gain contract. As an example, the owner hands the rancher a thousand heifer calves weighing 400 pounds each at the beginning of the year and pays the manager 16c a pound on all the gain these animals put on in the year. The manager furnishes everything including paying a land rent to the owner. If the manager furnishes less, the contract involves less cents per pound. These so-called "weight gain contracts" are gradually becoming the most common form of managerial incentive plan in the industry.
6. Occasionally the manager may be paid so many dollars per head on a flat fee to run the owner's cattle. This might be tied in with a weight gain contract as a "guaranteed minimum."
7. A common method used a number of years ago where the manager owned the land, the feed, and furnished the labor, was for the owner to put steers or calves and yearlings out on a "share the gain" basis. A certain number of cattle were purchased at a given price by the owner. The cattle would then be handed to the manager who would run them for a specified period of time, and the cattle would then be sold. The proceeds after the owner had been paid back his original cost would be split fifty-fifty between the

owner and the manager. The owner would be receiving a return for the capital that he had tied up for the period, and the manager would receive a return for his land, feed and labor out of the additional weight and gain that had been put on the cattle while they were in his possession. However, in this particular case, risks and profits from market fluctuations would be partially borne by the manager as well as the owner. In recent years operating costs have risen so high that the manager would normally demand more than a 50% share of the gain if he furnished everything except the cattle.

The game of wits between owner and manager has been going on ever since the days of Jacob and Laban. This is one reason that every detail of a contract should be spelled out word by word in writing. Items of apparently minor significance can be quite costly financially to the unwary.

For example, the term "gate cut" is commonly used to denote a technique of dividing cattle. If you are entitled to half of the calves proceeding along a road by a "gate cut" it would mean that after half of the calves had gone through a gate the gate would be closed and you would be entitled to the half that was on one side of the fence and the partner in your agreement would be entitled to the calves on the other side of the fence. However, if a group of calves were moving along a road and the march had been over two or three miles in duration, the biggest, strongest and best of the calves would be at the head of the column and the poor end of the calves would be at the rear. Consequently, on a "gate cut" the man who got the calves at the head of the column would probably have a group at least 20% more valuable than the rear half.

A much fairer method would be a "gate cut" from a group of animals in a corral. In this case the gate is open and a random half of the cattle which are milling around would be allowed to go through. Even here, the strongest and healthiest would tend to be out of the gate first. The only fair way is to let one-fourth of the cattle out which will belong to one party, let the second fourth out which will belong to the other party, then let a third fourth out which will belong to the first party, with the remaining fourth belonging to the other one.

An almost infallible way of dividing cattle when both parties are experts is to let party "A" divide the herd into what he thinks are two equal increments; then party "B" gets to select the group that he wants. There is almost no way of beating this particular arrangement.

In the newer and more lately settled sections of the country, the landowner as a separate private entity is a fairly new element. As previously mentioned, most lands until recently were publicly owned. After they became privately owned, they generally belonged to the man or family that owned the cattle. However, as time went on, much of the land went into the hands of estates, widows, or trusts, who wished to continue to hold the land as a stable investment but did not have the ability or the inclination to take the risks and hazards of operations and market fluctuations on the livestock itself. As the country gets older the grazing lease will become more and more common.

Grazing leases have an extremely negotiable market, and in a given area go up and down with the laws of supply and demand in a fairly uniform manner. While there are undoubtedly hundreds of variations, these three are the most common:

1. A given tract of ground is rented at so much per acre for a one to five year period. For some reason, leases over five years are very unusual. Normally the owner guarantees water, maintains fences, and pays real estate taxes.
2. The ranch is leased for the grazing season, usually six months, at so many dollars per head of livestock. To save labor costs, the lessee normally uses the property up to capacity, but will not overgraze because this will hurt his stock as much as it would the land.
3. The ranch owner takes cattle at so much per head per month. This is the most favorable for the lessee as he can move his cattle off in the event of a drought and will not get stuck for the rent on nonusable acreage. In the latter case, the ranch owner will demand and the herd owner is willing to pay a higher rent than if the contract exists for the entire year. The owner here also has the problem–if the lessee moves his herd off one month before the end of the grazing season–that nobody else will take the land as the costs of moving are prohibitive for so short a period, and he is out a month's rent.

It is difficult to compare grazing costs in different sections of the country, but it is easy to see that a north Missouri farm where a cow has to travel only three (3) acres to adequately support itself is worth twice as much as an Arizona ranch where it takes forty (40) acres to support an animal. The mere running from one isolated patch of grass to another would keep the weight down.

"The gains made during the summer by young cattle on pasture will, of course, vary greatly with the condition of the animals at the beginning of the grazing season and with the kind of forage provided.

Also, they will vary from year to year because of weather conditions, which greatly affect the amount and palatability of the forage. Occasionally a severe drought and the discomfort caused by flies and oppressive heat may result in a loss during mid-summer of a considerable amount of the gain put on during the spring. As a consequence, the gain for the entire season will be disappointingly small. However, such years are in the course of time offset by unusually favorable seasons, when the gains made are almost double those obtained during an average year.

"Yearling cattle weighing around 550 to 650 pounds when turned onto pasture will gain at the rate of 1-1/4 to 1-1/2 pounds a day on good permanent pasture like bluegrass, brome grass, or on the bluestem pastures of Kansas—or 200 to 250 pounds for the season. Two-year-olds will gain 50 to 75 pounds more if the forage is sufficiently abundant and nutritious to cause a noticeable improvement in degree of flesh, but 50 to 75 pounds less if it provides for only growth requirements. Rotation pastures that consist largely of legumes and hence retain their freshness and palatability throughout the summer may usually be counted on for about 50% more gain per head than is obtained from permanent pastures during the same season."[3]

To get a rough idea of the market in the Nebraska, South Dakota, Missouri area during the years 1952 to 1960, a six month grazing deal for a cow and its spring calf would run from $15.00 to $30.00. $15.00 would be a rip-snorting bargain; $30.00 would have been so high as to upset much chance of an operating profit.

While he hasn't particularly entered the livestock industry yet, there is a new man who has entered agriculture who represents a fourth element. We have the man who owns the cattle, the man who owns the land, the man who does the work, and within ten years we are going to have the man who owns the machinery. He might own it and operate it himself on a custom basis, or he might own it and lease it to the rancher. The present trend to ever larger, more complicated, and more expensive equipment is moving toward a point where only the very largest ranchers will be able to afford it themselves and give it complete utilization.

The smaller rancher will find that certain operations like putting up hay can be hired out to custom workers cheaper than he can possibly do it himself. All one has to do is to take a look at an Allis-Chalmers or International Harvester catalogue and see how fast he could spend $50,000. If, by any chance, the reader of this book were

[3]*Beef Cattle*, R. R. Snapp, 1952, p. 212.

Quannah Parker, the famous Indian Chief, who was employed in his later years by Dan Waggoner as a ranch hand. (Courtesy, *The Cattleman*, Fort Worth, Texas)

Chuckwagon about to roll on a North Texas ranch in 1897. (Courtesy, Rita Blanca Studio, Dalhart, Texas)

Herd near Belgrade, Montana. This is country where the cattle winter in low irrigated meadows and graze on the high government land in the summer. (Courtesy, American Angus Assn.)

A picture of Colonel Charles Goodnight taken in 1887. (Courtesy, Rita Blanca Studio, Dalhart, Texas)

Colonel C. C. Slaughter, President of the First National Bank of Dallas and the first native-born cattle king of Texas. (Courtesy, *The Cattleman,* Fort Worth, Texas)

familiar with farming or ranching fifteen years ago and has not had much contact with it since, he can multiply his recollection of equipment costs by about three and he won't be too far wrong. Repairs and maintenance have moved up at about the same proportion.

Chapter IX

Using Government Land

About 90% of the ranches in the United States today that have over a 1,000 cow capacity utilize land leased from the Federal Government, the State Government, or an institution such as a university or railroad. In order to avoid writing a separate volume on the subject, let us confine ourselves to the high points of leases on Federal land.

In the ten western states, where Federal grazing land is over 50% of the total area of the state, the bulk of the Federal leases fall into four general categories:

1. Bureau of Land Management Leases (BLM).
2. Forest Permits.
3. Department of Defense Leases.
4. Indian Leases.

Things have progressed a long way since the hired gunmen of the Bay State and the Swan shot homesteaders and government surveyors. In general, the BLM land (which was a successor to the old Taylor Grazing Act land) and the Forest Permits go at about one-fifth the rents charged on civilian leases for identical type land. On the other hand, the Indian Leases and the Department of Defense Leases have recently been put out at competitive sealed bids and the rents are pretty much on a par with civilian rents.

In the case of all four types of the leases, the government bureau doing the specific supervision is now preventing overgrazing and encouraging soil improvement without putting up with any nonsense from the lessees concerned. This is all a phenomenon of the last fifteen years and has been accomplished in the face of a lot of silent political pressure.

There has been an interesting historical evolution of Federal policy in regard to these lands in the last fifty years.

1. The government has always tried to maintain "integrated ranches." This is a case where the rancher has deeded land with the water holes and irrigated hay meadows but needs government summer pasture to carry the herd the balance of the year.
2. Because of the tremendous political power of the large land

owning ranchers, the government used every device to prevent outsiders coming in and getting the leases. Such devices included actually attaching leases or grazing permits to certain brands or tracts of deeded land. In the case of public sealed bids, it often took the form of letting the previous lessee have the right to match the winning bid and keep it. This discouraged bidders.

3. Another device was to let the land be put out for bid in small increments at varying times so no single tract would be a usable entity.

From President Cleveland's time on, various attempts were made to permanently let the Federal land go to the large ranchers, but this was consistently stopped by the eastern Congressmen. The recent demand from large population centers for recreational land and hunting preserves is gradually cutting down the grazing permits on the National Forest. Likewise, the increasing education of the Indian and his ability to stock his own reservations is cutting back the white man's leases from the Indian Bureau.

The *Bureau of Land Management* was set up by the Federal Range Code for Grazing Districts in January, 1956.

> Grazing districts will be administered to conserve and regulate the public grazing lands, to stabilize the livestock industry dependent upon them, and in aid thereof to promote the proper use of the privately controlled lands and waters dependent upon those public grazing lands. In furtherance of these objectives, grazing privileges will be granted with a view to the protection of those livestock operations that are recognized as established and continuing and which normally involve the substantial use of the public range in a regular, continuing manner each year. To promote the highest use of the public lands within grazing districts which have been or hereafter are established, possession or control of sufficient land or water to insure a year-round operation for a certain number of livestock in connection with the use of the Federal range will be required of all users."[1]

Certain permits on given tracts of land are organized on an animal unit per month basis (AUM). For example, if you had a permit to run 100 cows for five months on a given area, it would be called a 500 AUM permit.

Depending on the local ground rules, you might be permitted to run 200 cows for two and one-half months or you might not. Permits are for one year only, but are always renewed unless you have done something serious in violation of the rules. They may be increased or decreased from time to time and particularly after a change of ownership.

[1]The Federal Range Code for Grazing Districts, Section 161.1.

The permits are assigned on a very complicated priority system, but the most important is proximity of a deeded home ranch with water priority and winter feed production. Permits are bought and sold but there is no compensation on condemnation. When a permit is sold, it needs BLM permission to get it transferred to some other deeded land.

While some permits have been in the same family for 30 years, the fact that there is some jeopardy is evidenced by banks and insurance companies refusing to loan on them. In the event of the deeded land being leased for over a two year period, the permits can be leased too.

Forest Permits are probably the most closely supervised of all government leases and great care is taken to see that plenty of forage is left for game. Usually resident rangers see that every letter of the law is upheld. Normally the grazing is limited to about 50% of capacity which has caused a steady improvement of the grass cover. Permits are for so many head for a season. The permitted season is usually one month after normal so the spring grass has a good chance to get started.

Defense Department Leases are by public sealed bid. They are usually for five years with a cancellation clause by the lessee on ten days' notice and a cancellation by the government if the land is needed for military purposes.

Perimeter fences are usually outstanding and are maintained by the government. There are generally certain security regulations and elaborate fire precautions that cause some administrative problems. Often the bids will require mowing of nonused portions of the land as well as fence construction, fertilizing, reseeding, and other work. In recent years the Defense Department is more anxious to get the work done than to get cash rent. A careful analysis of the entire proposition must be made to submit an intelligent bid.

Indian Reservation Leases can be divided into three categories: (1) those made with the Department of Interior; (2) those made with the Tribal Council and approved by the Indian Bureau; and (3) those made with individual Indians which may or may not require approval by the Indian Bureau.

This particular field was formerly much abused and full of corruption, but has been gradually cleaned up over the last ten years. The first two categories are now generally public sealed bids on a per-head per-year basis with no monkey business. Futhermore, there is a cancellation clause that any white man can have all or part of his lease cancelled on six months' notice if any Indian wants the land and can show that he can stock it.

To my knowledge all Indian leases, even those made with private individuals, are limited by law to a five-year maximum. Futhermore, grazing is limited to about 60% of capacity, which protects the grass in the event of drought.

Since World War II, many of the younger Indians have been going to agricultural colleges and are gradually recapturing most of their reservation lands for their own use. They have also learned how to employ top notch lawyers to protect their interests.

When large western spreads change hands, sophisticated buyers make a careful appraisal of the security of the government leases. For example, if there were an all-deeded Arizona ranch of 1,000 head capacity, it might go for $750,000. If 50% of the land were deeded and 50% of the capacity were attached AUM's of the Bureau of Land Management, it might go for $550,000. If 50% were deeded and 50% were in a detached forest permit, it might go for $400,000. If 20% were deeded and the balance were Indian Bureau leases, it might go for $200,000.

The way the land lay would also be a matter of consideration. If the deeded land were checkerboarded in with the government lease and the deeded land had all of the winter facilities, your security would be much greater than if they were separated usable assembled tracts.

Chapter X

Tax Aspects of the Cattle Industry

Partially by the nature of the business and partially by the nature of the tax laws concerning it, the raising of livestock gets an income tax treatment in which even the basic principles differ from that afforded most other forms of American business. Occasionally these differences are less favorable, e.g., you must hold a breeding animal twelve (12) months instead of six (6) months to get the capital gain treatment, but the overwhelming majority of these differences are more favorable.

Most of the tax advantages apply to animals held for breeding purposes rather than feeders. As will be seen in a later chapter, a rancher or farmer can normally make a 20% better return on running steers rather than using his land for a breeding herd of commercial or registered cows. If part of the profit is to be derived from a constant effort to improve quality by scientifically upgrading the herd, then the strictly economic results will bear an even less favorable relation to the costs expended.

The above applies to the thousands of ordinary breeders and not to the 30 or 40 who have been particularly adept or lucky and have struck it rich. In a great many countries this situation has been recognized by the national governments who import bulls and run the better herds themselves, eventually distributing bull calves at nominal cost to the civilian farmers, as a public service.

In our country the government grants tax subsidies to encourage the improvement of breeding herds. In addition they make actual cash grants for research, disease control, and educational programs. While the term "tax loophole" or "tax gimmick" is occasionally applied to cattle, this is definitely not the case. The special provisions were purposefully *put into* the law, after long study between the proper congressional tax committees and the Department of Agriculture, to encourage private individuals to take over a program that would otherwise have to be handled directly by the government.

Cattle is often compared to oil as an investment. A 1953 *Business*

Week article compares Doe, the oil driller who has hit, with Doe, the potential rancher:

> "Of course, Doe was lucky. It might have been his ill fortune to end up with a tract full of dry holes. In that case, he would have lost a good sum of money no matter how much he was able to recoup in tax savings.
>
> "Suppose, back in 1952, this possibility has frightened him away from the oil business. He wanted to invest some money somewhere; the gambling urge was upon him; oil seemed risky, yet stocks and bonds weren't exciting enough. What could he have done? A likely answer: ranching. It isn't nearly so profitable as oil—but then it isn't so risky."[1]

Admitting that you can never parlay a $50,000 drilling expense into a $10,000,000 oil field strike, what is it about cattle that might appeal to a conservative investor over oil?

These are the obvious points:

1. The cattle are on top of the ground and he can see them and count them; the oil is under the ground and he can't see it nor determine for certain how much is there.
2. Within a 20% plus or minus margin he can tell how many calves his maintenance expense on a breeding herd will produce and how much weight his feed expenses will put on his yearlings.
3. Within a 3% plus or minus margin he can predict how disasters or diseases can affect the mortality rate. If he feels nervous about this, Lloyd's of London will insure his animals against "death from any cause" and charge him a premium of 3% on his herd valuation, with a 3% deductible.

The following are some tax points for cattlemen:

1. When you buy animals to fatten and resell at an increased weight and price you are in a "feeding operation." Your feed and maintenance is deductible and any gain is taxable at straight income tax rates. You are not allowed any depreciation on the animals.
2. Animals that are capable of breeding (bulls and cows, but not steers), that are kept in a herd for the purpose of producing calves, can be depreciated, and when they are held for over twelve (12) months, if sold at a profit, such profit will be taxed at capital gain rates. In this case it is necessary to establish with the Internal Revenue Department that it was your "intent" to go into the *cattle breeding* business as opposed to the *cattle feeding* business.
3. Calves sold from a breeding herd are taxed at regular income tax rates except when they are sold as part of a herd dispersal. In this case, you are not selling "animals," but are selling your cattle breed-

[1] "Texas Millionaires, How They Work It," *Business Week,* Dec., 1953, p. 77.

ing business and you are taxed at capital gain rates.
4. Bull calves may be exchanged for heifer calves; cows may be exchanged for bulls. These are tax free exchanges.
5. Feed, maintenance, pasture rents, etc. may be paid for a year in advance and *deducted in the year paid.* Within reason you can buy sufficient extra feed to allow for normal contingencies such as drought, flood, crop failure, severe winter, etc.
6. A perfectly normal operation would be for a man to be both a breeder and a feeder. His breeding herd is producing calves which he in turn either feeds or contracts for a feed lot to do for him. One group of animals is taxed as a breeding herd; the other operation as a feeding deal.
7. Technically as soon as an animal is "mature," it can be considered part of your breeding herd and eligible for depreciation. If "maturity" can be interpreted as when it is capable of being bred, eight months should do the trick although this would certainly be a very poor practice. Naturally only animals purchased can be depreciated, and the base would be the original purchase price. For the purpose of this book we will consider only those operators on the cash basis and forget the accrual basis.
8. For breeding cattle, the Internal Revenue Department will accept an eight year longevity for depreciation. Obviously some discretion has to be used. If you purchase a seven year old cow, you can't write her off in one year. Once a cow has reached seven years in age in a good healthy condition, she can probably produce for another four years. In the case of valuable registered animals closely supervised on a small farm, you might get calf production up to fifteen years or longer.
9. Loss by death from any cause is fully deductible in the year that it occurs and does not have to be treated as a long term capital loss.
10. Insurance premiums are fully deductible, but any recovery is taxable according to the animal that died. For example, if you recover $100 on a calf that died which you had raised and which stood at zero on your books, you would have to pay full income tax on the $100. If you recovered $500 on a bull for which you paid $500 it would be return of capital and not taxable except to the extent you had depreciated the bull.
11. Animals normally "culled" from a breeding herd and sold at a profit over depreciated value are taxable at capital gain rates. Obviously this is another practice, which, if carried to extremes, particularly on younger animals, would be disallowed by the Treasury Department.

12. Despite the fact that profits made on the sale of animals in the breeding herd held over 12 months are taxable as long term capital gains, any *losses* derived from the sale of these animals are to be entered on separate Schedule D, Form 1040, "(2) Property other than Capital Assets." From there the loss should be transferred to Form 1040, Page 2, Schedule D, Line 2, where it would be fully deductible.[2] "Net losses on these Capital Assets are deductible in full and are not subject to the limitation of $1,000 per year as are net losses on other capital assets."[3]

13. In the case where a person's main business is not cattle breeding but is derived from other activities, if he loses more than $50,000[4] per year in cattle breeding for five consecutive years, he could have his excess losses above $50,000 recomputed and disallowed. Further, if he has suffered a net operating loss deduction from all of his business activities, that portion of the total net operating loss caused by the cattle breeding business where he has lost $50,000 for five consecutive years will not be allowed.[5]

This section was actually designed for people operating "hobbies" rather than legitimate businesses, e.g., racing stables, luxurious country estates labeled farms, yachts, etc.

14. Another change in the 1954 tax bill considerably liberalizes the preceding provision:

"(1) House changes accepted by committee. Under present law, if losses from a trade or business exceed $50,000 a year for five consecutive years only $50,000 of the annual loss may be off-set against income from other sources and the portion of annual loss above $50,000 is disallowed. . . . However, the present provision may in some instances penalize bona fide business enterprises, such as farms suffering drought, mining businesses with large development costs and businesses incurring casualty and abandonment losses.

"To avoid such results, the House and your Committee's bill removed from the application of this provision losses and expenses incurred by farmers because of drought, casualty and abandonment losses and expenditures which may, at the taxpayer's option, either be capitalized or be deducted when incurred. Deductions for these items are to be omitted in computing the amount of the taxpayer's

---

[2]*Farmers Income Tax 1954,* Monatt's Sect. 131, p. 43.

[3]*Idem,* Sect. 132, p. 45.

[4]In a joint return where husband and wife both participate in the operation, this can be increased to $100,000.

[5]*Internal Revenue Code of 1954,* Chapter 1, Section 270 (a) Commerce Clearing House, Inc., p. 94.

loss for the purpose of determining whether he had a loss in excess of $50,000. Moreover, these deductions are to be allowed even if the taxpayer's losses exceed $50,000 a year for five consecutive years. Otherwise, an unusually large loss in one year might have the effect of creating losses in five consecutive years and bringing the taxpayer within this provision.

"The treatment provided for the net operating loss differs from that provided for the other specially treated deductions in that if a taxpayer is subject to this provision a deduction for the net operating loss will not be allowed.

"Your committee also made it clear that the changes made by the House and your committee in this provision are applicable only with respect to years in a period of five consecutive years, one or more of which begins after December 31, 1953."[6]

15. "*Section 172 (b)–Net operating loss carry-backs and carry-overs.*"

"1. Years to which loss may be carried–a net operating loss for any taxable year ending after December 31, 1953, shall be–

(A) A net loss carryback to each of the two taxable years preceding the taxable year of such loss, and

(B) A net operating loss carryover to each of the five taxable years following the taxable year of such loss."[7]

16. It is possible to sell a breeding herd on the installment plan and only pay capital gain tax on a pro-rated amount of the gain which is actually received in the specific year provided that the total value of the herd exceeds $1,000 and the down payments and other payments do not exceed 30% of the selling price.[8]

17. Under Section 1033 of the Internal Revenue Code where property is involuntarily converted into similar property or money as a "result of the destruction in whole or in part, death, seizure, or requisition or condemnation or imminence thereof" and you buy property of a similar kind with the money within one year after the close of the first taxable year in which any part of the gain upon the conversion is realized then you don't have to pay any tax on the gain.

---

[6]Revenue Code of 1954, H.R. 8300, Senate Committee Report explaining the changes made by the finance committee in the House, passed Internal Revenue Code of 1954. *Standard Federal Tax Report Extra Edition,* Vol. XLI, No. 29, June 30, 1954, p. 40.

[7]*Internal Revenue Code of 1954,* Section 172, Commerce Clearing House, Inc., p. 76.

[8]*Idem,* Section 453 (b), p. 165.

In addition to the preceding, which existed prior to 1954, the new 1954 Code added Section 1033 (e) as follows:

"*Livestock Destroyed by Disease*"

"For purposes of this subtitle, if livestock are destroyed by or on account of disease, or are sold or exchanged, they shall be treated as an involuntary conversion to which this section applies." Specifically, if you had raised $10,000 worth of heifer yearlings from a herd of your own, which, if sold would require the paying of direct income taxes on the money, and there was an outbreak of Bangs in your herd which necessitated your selling your cattle; then, in the event you repurchased a similar herd within one year from the end of your tax year, with the $10,000 that you received, you will not have to pay any tax.[9]

18. A ruling is now being requested of the Internal Revenue Bureau as to whether the accelerated methods of depreciation in Section 167 of the new code will apply to breeding cattle as well as to other forms of property. In the event that it does, it will have a major impact on the industry and will probably cause investment in a higher quality of breeding stock than was formerly customary.

One of the new forms of taking depreciation is the so-called "declining balance" method. Here's how this will work if you bought a registered $1,000 bull, one year old.

Under the former "straight-line method" you would have to depreciate him at 12½% a year or $125 per year. Now under the declining balance method you are allowed to depreciate 25% the first year or $250. The second year you subtract $250 from the $1,000 leaving you a balance of $750; take 25% of the remainder and this is your depreciation for the second year. Again you subtract the second year's depreciation from the remaining balance and take 25% for the third year.[10]

There has been some controversy among my associates as to whether or not this would apply to the purchase of a breeding animal 4 or 5 years old which had been raised as a calf by the original owner and never sold and never depreciated by the original owner. Would this be a piece of "new equipment" which it must be to qualify under the new law? Quoting from the Senate Report: "The liberalized depreciation methods provided in the bills are to apply to all types of tangible depreciable assets, including all farm equipment, machinery, and buildings, rental housing, and industrial and

[9] *Idem*, p. 309.
[10] *Idem*, Section 167 (b), p. 64.

commercial buildings, as well as machinery and equipment. They are limited, however, to property new in use and therefore never before subject to depreciation allowances."[11] However, in the technical discussion of the bill in the Senate Report is this: "Property which is described in Paragraph (c) includes property acquired after December 31, 1953, but only if the original use of the property is commenced with the taxpayer and is commenced after that date. Thus, such property must be new in use, that is, never before having been subject to depreciation *whether or not depreciation deductions relating to such property were allowable.*"[12] The new code allows the accelerated depreciation schedule to be applied only to property with a useful life of three or more years.

Whether or not it was the intention of Congress to include breeding herds in Section 167, it actually makes a very logical application of the law, possibly more so than in some cases of equipment and machinery. For example:

A. The $1,000 registered bull referred to previously will be able to service 30 cows in inexpensive pasture breeding from the age of two to five.

B. From the ages of five to seven he can adequately service possibly 25 cows.

C. From the age of seven to ten he will not be able to get around so well and breeding will have to be accomplished by expensive artificial methods or by close-in supervised and troublesome pen operations.

D. Somewhere after ten years his productivity will not justify his expensive maintenance and he will be sent to the meat market where he will bring somewhere around $150.

Here we have a situation where each year the activity decreases, the expenses of maintenance and operation increases, and with an eventual salvage value as meat this almost perfectly fits the theory of the declining balance method. By a quick write-off occurring in the years of high productivity and least expense, many a rancher should feel justified in purchasing a higher quality bull than he would under the old method. This cannot help but have a beneficial effect on the quality of breeding herds over the country, an objective for which the Department of Agriculture and the various state agricultural schools have been striving for some time.

[11] *Senate Committee Report on Revenue Code of 1954,* Standard Clearing House, Inc., p. 25.

[12] *Idem,* p. 203.

19. To get the favored tax treatment afforded a cattle breeder on a specific animal you do not actually have to use it as such if you can establish that it was your *intent* to do so and you were prevented from doing it by circumstances beyond your control. Fairly complicated situations can arise in this regard such as the following examples from Monatt's Farmers Income Tax Book of 1954:

A. "White is in the business of raising registered cattle for sale to others for use by them as breeding cattle. It is the business' practice for the cattle to be bred, prior to sale, in order to establish their fitness for sale as registered breeding cattle.

"Result: Those cattle used by White to produce calves which are added to White's herd are held for breeding purposes.

"White's use of the other cattle for breeding purposes is an ordinary or necessary incident to his holding of such other cattle for the purpose of selling them as registered breeding cattle, and such use does not *demonstrate* that White is holding the cattle for breeding purposes.

B. "Brown, engaged in the business of buying cattle and fattening them for slaughter, purchased cows with calf. The calves were born while the cows were held by Brown.

"Result: The cows were not held for breeding purposes."[13]

C. "White retires from the breeding or dairy business and sells his entire herd, including young animals which would have been used by him for breeding or dairy purposes if he had remained in business.

"Result: These young animals were held for breeding or dairy purposes."

Some Recent Tax Decisions on Cattle:

1. *Prothro, Campbell, Jr. vs. Collector.*
Judgment of District Court, #73, 302 P-H Fed. 1953, affirmed by U. S. Court of Appeals, Fifth Circuit, No. 14411, Jan. 6, 1954.

In an oversimplified form this case involved Mr. Prothro giving 100 calves he had raised to the Wichita Falls YMCA. He had previously deducted the cost of raising them and he took a second deduction as a charitable gift when he gave them away.

The collector contended that the gift of the calves was a gift of "realized income" and as such was taxable to Prothro.

The judge who found in favor of Prothro said in his concurring opinion: "We come back, then to the point of departure. Were the

[13]Monatt's *Farmers Income Tax 1954,* Commerce Clearing House, Inc. p. 118.

calves, when transferred by gift to the YMCA, realized income to the appellees in the taxable sense? We think it clear that they were not. If they were, then every appreciation in value of property passing by gift is realized income. We know that this is not so, and that, though it is and has been the contention of the Bureau that it ought to be, Congress has never enacted legislation so providing."[14]

The implications here are obvious to a man in a 90% bracket who is contemplating disbursing his breeding herd or giving some of his herd to charity. If he sells all the animals he has raised himself, they stand him at zero on his books, and he must pay 25% capital gains tax. If he gives these same animals to charity he will get a 100% write off against other income or a recovery of 90% as opposed to a 75% recovery after capital gains tax. This is a net gain to him of 15%.

2. *James M. MacDonald vs. Commissioner of Internal Revenue.* Court of Appeals Decision reversing Tax Court decision of August 14, 1951. This case involves the capital gains treatment of culls from a breeding herd and shows how by establishing his motives, intent, and procedures by careful records that the taxpayer was able to get a favorable decision as opposed to that given in the case of Walter S. Fox, 16 T. C. 854 affirmed Fox vs. C.I.R., 4 Cir., 198F. 2nd 719.

Both MacDonald and Fox sold a considerable number of younger animals from their breeding herds of varying ages. There were two principal points involved here. First, the quantity of animals eliminated tended to be higher than the average culling operation; and second, the quantity under 24 months of age made the collector question whether they were really part of the breeding herd or "animals held for sale."

In the case of Fox, "the age at which they sold their young animals depended on the varying preferences and desires of purchasers." MacDonald, by his careful records and procedures, established that, "animals were sold only if, as, and when they evidenced undesirable characteristics."[15] In this connection the Court also pointed out that the Court of Appeals' opinion in the Fox case emphasized the regularity and high proportion of sales and the failure of the taxpayers to test the breeding qualities of animals

[14]*Federal Tax Report Bulletin,* Prentice-Hall, Inc., 1954, 1-14-54, No. 2—127 #72, 241.

[15]MacDonald vs. C.I.R., opinion of Clark, Circuit Judge, "Court of Appeals Rules That Motive Is the All-Important Factor," in Capital Gains Case, *The Hereford Journal* of Oct. 1, 1954, p. 32.

before disposing of them.

The Court stated that it felt the Fox case ruling penalized breeders with skill sufficient to detect and cull inferior animals before they had been bred, thereby agreeing with the taxpayer's contention that even at the age of seven months it was possible for taxpayers to make intelligent selections. The Court stated that the evidence was compelling that such early selection could be accurately made. (See footnote 15 on preceding page.)

3. A cash basis farmer or rancher filing a calendar year return may be the only class of individual in the United States who can deduct a major part of his following year's operating expenses in the fall of the current year. This is occasioned by the fact that it is a one hundred and fifty year old custom in the industry in the United States for a farmer at harvest time in October and November to purchase his feed and pasture for the coming year.

There has never been any problem on this point where the farmer or rancher had sufficient cattle on hand to actually consume the feed and pasture over the coming winter and spring. However, there are some court decisions favoring the taxpayer on this point where either the farmer did not have the livestock on hand to consume the purchase, failed to consume it the following year, or never did consume it.

In the case of O'Malley (Collector) vs. Cover, wheat was purchased on December 31, 1942 at a cost of $27,000 for the purpose of feeding cattle to be acquired. It was deducted as ordinary and necessary expense although it could not be used in 1943 for the purpose for which it was bought and it was resold in 1944.[16]

In the case of R. D. and Ida M. Cravens vs. the Commissioner of Internal Revenue in the year 1953, Cravens, a cattle raiser, made an advance payment of $50,000 to a feed company for its promise to him of preferential treatment of future deliveries of scarce cattle feed. The $50,000 was to be applied against current market price of the delivered feed. The payment was made in 1953 and the deliveries were not completed until 1956. The question was whether the entire $50,000 was a deductible business expense in the year paid. In a reversal of the tax court's decision, the U. S. Court of Appeals (10th Circuit) felt that the payment protected the taxpayer against a distress liquidation of his herd in future years due to feed scarcity and was deductible in the year paid although the

[16]O'Malley (Collector) vs. Cover, (C. A. 8, 1955) 221F 2nd 156, 55-1 U. S. T. C. 54, 756.

The famous railroad financier Mr. Jay Gould who got five million acres of Texas land for laying the line of the Texas and Pacific Railroad. (Courtesy, Library of Congress)

Commission men and order buyers going down the alley at a large central stockyards. (Courtesy, American Hereford Assn.)

Public auctions conducted with glamor and showmanship have become a major method of marketing cattle.

Calf crop percentages can run from 75% on a large western ranch to 90% on a small Midwestern farm. (Courtesy, American Hereford Assn.)

The degree to which cattle are fed, the class of cattle that are fed, and the ultimate price that is paid at each stop along the line is determined by the housewife standing across from the retail butcher counter. (Courtesy, Safeway Stores, Inc., Publicity Dept.)

Many cattle breeders are also in the feeding business. However, there are no tax advantages for feeders. (Courtesy, American Hereford Assn.)

Once a cow has had a calf, it is no longer "new in use" and is not eligible for accelerated depreciation. (Courtesy, American Hereford Assn.)

actual feed might not be physically delivered for a couple of years thereafter. This decision was rendered despite the tax court's findings that the last of the feed to make up the $50,000 worth was not actually delivered until 1956.[17]

4. Approximately half of the tax litigation in the livestock industry concerns "intent" as to whether the cattle were held for breeding purposes or for resale. In both of the following cases the taxpayers position had been considerably weakened by the fact that advertisements for the sale of breeding stock were constantly being run in various of the national trade magazines.

"All members of the American Hereford Association and the American Polled Hereford Association will find the Hancock decision, CCH Dec. 23, 408, 31 TC–, No. 77, interesting reading. Compare it with the Clark case, CCH Dec. 22, 302, 27 TC 1006. The Hancock decision involves a taxpayer who started a breeding herd (it grew from 23 to 525 animals in a few years). The taxpayer was engaged in the process of building a prime breeding herd of registered Polled Hereford cattle. His only herd was devoted to the achievement of that end. He was constantly striving to improve its quality through selective breeding practices and through continual culling of undesirables. Every animal acquired, whether by birth or purchase, was considered by him to be part of that breeding herd. If it developed a defect which rendered it unsuitable for use in the herd, it was culled and placed in a pasture apart therefrom to await its ultimate disposition. Had the animal not developed the undesirable characteristic, it would have continued to have been held for the purpose of being put to use in the breeding herd.

"The tax problem concerns the sale of those animals culled from the herd. On these, the taxpayer took Section 117(j) (1), that is, long-term gain. The Commissioner says that the taxpayer's operations clearly indicate that he was in the business of selling breeding cattle, and not merely a casual vendor of inferior animals culled from his breeding herd. He contends that the cattle culled were held by the taxpayer for sale to customers in the ordinary course of that business.

"The Tax Court held that the taxpayer's culling of the undesirables from the breeding herd, segregation of the culls from that herd until disposition and sale of only the culled animals—and a

[17]R. D. & I. M. Cravens. U. S. Commissioner of Internal Revenue, U. S. Court of Appeals, 10th Circuit No. 6138, 11-25-59, *Federal Tax Report Bulletin*, Prentice-Hall.

continual increase of the size of the breeding herd—do not change the character of the animals sold from cattle held for breeding purposes to cattle held for sale to customers in the ordinary course of business."[18]

"Objection overruled. The witness may answer. The question is, were you always with the regular herd, or were you always with the breeding herd, or were you part of the time with each; and if the latter, tell us each date of transfer."

In connection with one of the cases a judge stated a personal opinion which is liable to be used in future cases. He said that in his mind absolute irrefutable evidence of a taxpayer's "intent to hold for breeding purposes" was whether or not the taxpayer had held the cattle long enough to have bred them, produced a calf crop, and rebred them. This statement, of course, goes considerably beyond the wording of Section 1231 of the 1954 Code, but it will undoubtedly be widely quoted by reviewing agents. Had a definition as strong as this been accepted, the taxpayer would have lost everyone of the breeding herd cases, including the famous MacDonald case.

[18]*TAXES—The Tax Magazine*, March 1959, pp. 200-201.

Chapter XI

Cattle and the Law

Insofar as agricultural land was the first form of real property and livestock the original and most important form of personal property, about half of all cases in the English and American courts prior to 1900 are tied in with one of these two elements.

In this chapter we shall limit ourselves to certain laws, regulations, and customs of interest to operating ranchers and peculiar to the livestock business that are not common to all forms of property. In a previous chapter we covered tax laws and later we will discuss chattel mortgages. Here we will touch on the following:

1. Public Liability.
2. Fencing.
3. Brands and Ownership.
4. Interstate Transportation.

It must be emphasized that there is a substantial difference in county and state laws and sometimes these conflict with Federal laws. Also there is a substantial difference from area to area in what is on the books and what is enforced. For example, there are complete state statutes in Missouri on branding but for the last 50 years less than 10% of the cattle in the state have actually been branded. In this chapter no attempt will be made to pinpoint the specific situation at a given spot, but just to give a general picture over the country.

In regard to public liability, let us take the specific example of A's bull, being run on B's ranch, by a lessee, C, which gores D. In any case, D will undoubtedly sue A, B, and C. As between A, B, and C, the exact terms of the leases and management contracts will be significant as there are usually clauses about who assumes liability, who furnishes liability insurance, who is co-insured, who is an employee or contract laborer, etc.

The bigger problem is the status of D.

"An owner of domestic animals may be held liable for personal injuries caused by them in two general situations:

"a. When he negligently allows or causes them to commit the injury.

"b. When he is aware that an animal owned by him is vicious, and when such an animal bites, strikes, kicks, or gores someone who was not acting negligently.

"When hunters or other persons come on farm property without the consent of the owner, they are classed as trespassers and cannot be heard to complain if they are injured by the owner's animals. He owes such persons no duty other than not willfully to injure them. But if a hunter asks for permission to hunt and it is granted, and the owner fails to warn him of a bull or some other animal of a vicious nature, liability for injury may result. Also, under certain circumstances, the law views trespass by children in a different light. If, for example, an owner knows that youngsters from a nearby school or village, or even from a neighboring farm, are in the habit of playing in his pasture, and he keeps a mean animal in the pasture, he may very well be liable for injuries which result. On the other hand, adults who have a right to be on the farm, but who know of the vicious nature of the animal (a hired man or a neighbor, for example) may not be allowed to recover if they are injured."[1]

Litigation from livestock getting into a neighbor's grain field probably goes back to 3000 B.C. English common law, which applies on this point to most states east of the Mississippi, requires the owner of the cattle to *fence them in*. He is liable for any damage they do when they get out. In some western range states, however, it is the job of the crop owner to *fence out* any neighboring animals and the owner of the animals is not liable.

On this point there is the interesting phenomenon in some western spreads of "controlled land." For example, you might have an arid district that can support only 10 cows to a section. Let us suppose that 50 years ago, some family homesteaded a 640 acre section in the middle of a big ranch owned or leased by other parties and subsequently abandoned it. The heirs retained title but the fences collapsed. It is too dry to farm and no one could fence it to just run 10 cows. The fencing would cost more than the land.

The owner of the surrounding land lets his cattle roam over it and may or may not pay a nominal rent. If the owner of the "island" objects, the surrounding land owner says, "Well, fence my cattle out."

In more settled areas where grain farmers dominate the legislatures, there are very elaborate fencing laws. On division fences between two properties, the fence can be divided by facing it from your side with you being responsible for the half on your right. If your neighbor won't maintain and repair his half and you do your half, you can sometimes do it for him and sue him for your costs. In some cases, a farmer who does not maintain his half of a partition fence cannot sue for damages if his neighbor's cattle damage his crops.

[1]*Law for the Veterinarian and Livestock Owner*, Hannah and Storm, The Interstate Printers & Publishers, Inc., 1959, p. 119.

Ownership or title can be legally established by recording a bill of sale or, in most western states, by branding the hide with an officially registered brand. This recording of brands is usually handled by a state brand board or the state sanitary commission. In some states, e.g., Texas, it is done on a county basis, through the auspices of a cattlemen's association.

The big cattle states often maintain an inspector at all of the major stockyards. Also they maintain brand inspection stations on all major highways leaving the state. Some states require an inspection of hides at all slaughter houses with severe penalties for slaughtering at remote places, so as to prevent theft. Defacing brands, superimposing new brands on old ones, using non-registered brands are all matters for fine and imprisonment.[2]

> "A recorded cattle brand is prima facie, but not conclusive, evidence of ownership. Though a statute may require branding, failure to do so does not give another the right to affix his brand. In a Montana case, the court held that a bill of sale was not sufficient proof of ownership where the animal in question bore the uncancelled brand of a third party, and a chattel mortgage including this animal and executed by the third party was on file in the office of the Montana Livestock Commission. A brand owned by a partnership cannot be used by any of the partners on animals belonging only to him, unless the right is assigned to him by the other partners. Under a statute penalizing the misbranding of livestock belonging to another, or the willful defacing or obliterating of any brand upon 'any livestock,' the quoted words were held to include all livestock, regardless of ownership. However, in prosecutions under such a statute, the intent to claim an animal belonging to another must be proved beyond a reasonable doubt."[3]

Movements of cattle across a state line are controlled by regulations that may be issued from time to time by the Department of Agriculture or any applicable Federal law. The Federal government may prescribe standards of sanitation for equipment and premises, procedures to be followed, if diseased or exposed animals are carried, and rules regarding quarantine when animals are unloaded.[4]

The "28 hour law" refers to the provision that all animals in interstate shipment must be unloaded and fed every 28 hours. On intermediate hauls this has given trucking companies an advantage over scheduled railroads.[5]

[2] *The Stockman's Handbook*, M. E. Ensminger, The Interstate Printers & Publishers, Inc., Danville, Ill., 1959, p. 616.

[3] *Law for the Veterinarian and Livestock Owner*, p. 130.

[4] *Idem*, p. 78.

[5] *Idem*, p. 79.

PART III

ECONOMICS

Chapter XII

Ranching as a Business

With stocks at an all time high, government bonds in a state of depression, and inflation noises from all sides, ranch and farm brokers throughout the nation are seeing a sudden rising tide of investment demand for agricultural and grazing land. For the first time in recent history this demand is coming not from the man who wants a country hobby or a weekend place for his children to ride horseback, but from sophisticated investors who have been in dozens of kinds of businesses and have ridden all types of securities up and down the various business cycles of the last thirty years. What is happening is a phenomenon of major consequence. One of our clients, a nationally known industrialist who has been to Europe more times than he has been west of the Alleghenies, crystallizes the attitude of many investors:

> "Land is the only thing in the U. S. that can't be manufactured. You can issue more common stocks but you can't issue more land. Top grade securities are now selling on 3% of earnings and you can get better rents from a farm. Urban land districts are subject to broad fluctuations. In ranch and farm land this is possible but not likely. This ranch I bought is large enough to rate a top level executive. If things get tough enough, I'll move out and run it myself."

Before a corporation executive gives up his desk and pine paneled office for the wide open spaces, however, he would do well to consider his chances of making a large tract of land stand on its own feet in the competitive investment market. Let us disregard all of the glamorous windfalls such as oil and uranium; or the expectation of the government buying his property for an Air Base; or the possibility of selling sub-division lands at fantastically inflated prices. Let us also disregard federal handouts such as ASC payments, the soil conservation program, or special subsidies accorded by the income tax laws.

In this chapter we shall look at the business of beef cattle. This phase of American agriculture, long bound by custom and tradition, is being affected by the most dramatic revolution in its history.

Until five years ago, Marshall Dillon, Wyatt Earp, and Buffalo Bill could have reappeared on an average western ranch and noted only the slightest of changes since the railroad got to Dodge City.

Starting with the drought and market collapse of 1953 and probably extending into 1965, the changes are going to be roughly comparable to the difference between a World War I bomber and the latest thing going up from Cape Canaveral.

As is often said of war, the principles remain the same but the techniques and methods of execution change. In the case of beef cattle ranching, potential investors will find the principles deceivingly simple. It is the application and interpretation of the basics that will bring to novices either pain or profit. As in his primary business endeavor, our executive will be faced with a capital investment, costs of production, and a product. His capital investment is land, equipment, and a breeding herd. His costs are made up of feed, labor and management. And his product is pounds of animals delivered to a point of sale. It is obvious that if the value of his product does not exceed his costs plus a reasonable allowance for depreciation of his equipment and breeding herd, he will not have a competitive investment.

This chapter is going to be divided into the following:

1. An Analysis of Ranch Expenses.
2. An Analysis of Ranch Product.
3. Variations in Operation Over the U. S.
4. Mathematical Conclusions and the Future.
5. Summary.

1. RANCH EXPENSES

Expenses can be grouped under the categories of feed, labor, equipment, management, and miscellaneous. Most ranch land currently rents on a 5% net basis and real estate taxes run a minimum of 1% of value. Consequently, whether an investor owns it or leases it, 6% of land values should be thrown into the equation. It might be well to evaluate the economics involved in the acquisition by an absentee owner of a 3,000 acre ranch in the Kansas blue stem. Three hundred acres are in alfalfa and corn and the rest is native pasture.

In this country it takes six acres to support a cow all year round. This also takes in the cow's spring calf. During the latter part of the summer the calf will graze as well as nurse but the entire package is called an "animal unit." The cultivated land is used to produce hay and grain to carry the cow through the winter. All of this is part of the six acres. This kind of land is now selling for about $75 per acre. Multiply this amount by the six acres and you arrive at a price on this ranch of approximately $450 per animal unit. This is the traditional way you equate a ranch in Montana with one in Florida, but it doesn't tell the whole story as you will see.

At six acres to an animal unit this ranch has a capacity of 500 cows. If you owned it or if you rented it and agreed to maintain the fences, you would have a land expense made up of taxes, maintenance, etc. of about $32 per cow. (In the case of ownership we assume you are entitled to 5% on your land.)

Your manager will cost you $6,000 per year which breaks down to $12 per head. ($6,000 ÷ 500.)

The owner will also need a $3,000 per year cowhand and temporary labor costing $1,000 for use during roundups and special occasions. In the old days, neighboring ranches exchanged labor and the roundup was the scene of a large scale social event, but that day is a thing of the past. A big ranch with 20 hands hesitates to accept help from the neighbor with two men for fear of having to reciprocate. The unofficial records that such exchanges entail prove extremely cumbersome.

If the ranch is producing its own hay and a small amount of corn, our investor will need $2,000 more for temporary hay crews and custom farm labor. Total labor costs, therefore, come out to $6,000 or another $12 per head. (This figure includes such items as maintenance on personal living quarters and cost of utilities.)

Yearly feed costs will include 200 pounds of protein supplement such as cottonseed cake at 4c per lb. for a total of $8 per cow and extra hay over that which is produced on the ranch at $2. Salt and minerals will cost an additional $2, bringing total feed costs to $12 per animal.

A typical operation will require a passenger car costing $2,000, a 1/2-ton pickup truck costing $1,500; tractor, wagon, baler, rake and other equipment costing $3,500; horses, saddles, harnesses, wagons, etc. costing $1,000. These items totalling $8,000 will depreciate at $2,000 per year, will need $2,000 in repairs, and will consume approximately $2,000 in gasoline, adding $6,000 or $12 per head in equipment costs to the total.

Personal property taxes will cost $1.50 per head while veterinary medicine and vet fees will come to 50c per head. Whether the owner has his own bulls, depreciates them, and pays maintenance on them or leases them, he will spend $10 per head on breeding costs. This assumes that it takes one bull to 22 cows in the area. These miscellaneous expenses come to $12 per head.

In summary, on a 500 cow Kansas ranch in the year 1959 this would be about par for the course:

Item	*Cost per Cow Unit*
Land, rent, land maintenance, real estate taxes	$32
Top management	12
Labor (permanent and temporary)	12
Feed (not produced on ranch)	12
Equipment	12
Miscellaneous (includes $10 breeding fee on bulls)	12
	$92

Total cost of year's operation on 500 cows—$46,000.

If the owner lived on the ranch and operated it, he could be his own "top manager." If he lived in a neighboring town and could check the place once a week, he might get by with a $300 per month manager rather than a $500 per month man. This analysis, however, is drawn up for a man living in New York who owns a Kansas ranch as an investment.

Another very significant item is the breeding cow herd itself. If a 3 year old cow costs $250 and an 11 year old canner is worth $90, such an investment depreciates $20 per year. ($250 minus $90 = $160. Divide by 8 years = $20.) Spread over 500 cows this gives an additional hidden depreciation cost of $10,000 per year, bringing the overall operation cost to $56,000.

2. VALUE OF PRODUCT

The product of such an operation, of course, is calves, whether they are retained to expand the herd or sold at market. In August 1959, mixed heifer and steer calves weighing about 400 lbs. were being contracted for delivery in November of 1959 at around $140 each. (35c per lb.)

In the Kansas blue stem you are doing a good job if you can produce an 85% calf crop of weaned calves out of a cow herd. On a herd of 500, this would be 425 calves. At $140 each, they would be worth $59,500. Cost of transportation to markets, commissions, etc. would probably come to $5 per head, giving our investor a net delivered gross of around $57,000. His operating costs including a 5% return on the land come to $56,000 making it a very tight squeeze.

It would also be well to consider that hazards are all on the other side. There is more chance that the calf crop will be under 85% rather than over; more chance that they will average under 400 lbs. than over; and particularly, in my opinion, that the market will go down to $130 rather than up to $150.

3. VARIATIONS IN OPERATION OVER THE UNITED STATES

Sooner or later the shrewd rancher investor comes to the realization that there are no bargains in this business. One area of the country averages out with another. If Arizona land costs about half as much per cow unit of capacity as Montana land and one could produce the same kind of calf crop at the same cost and both had the same transportation costs, and markets were similar—one of two things would happen: Arizona land would go up or Montana land would go down.

Let us compare the Kansas blue stem with northeastern Arizona. The Arizona land can be purchased at $100 per animal unit less, making rent or land cost 25% less. On the other hand, it takes 40 acres to run a cow instead of the six in Kansas so that ranchers have much greater areas of fence to purchase and maintain. In this country one bull can service only 18 cows instead of 22 because of the greater distances involved. Breeding costs, therefore, increase while the calf crop drops down. However, you do not have to feed much hay because of the milder winters but you need more proteins. These conditions substantially reduce labor costs in both hay production and winter feed distribution.

On the sale of the product in this region, ranchers do not have access to the great midwestern grain producing feeder areas and have to accept about $10 per head less in price. Here, cattle take a greater shrink than in Kansas in going to market because of the greater distances, and every third year will bring a drought bringing the calf crop down to a 325 lb. average. In Kansas, on the other hand, the batting average on drought would be about one in seven.

Again, using the Kansas blue stem as a point of reference, let us take a typical Wyoming ranch running 30 acres to the cow for summer pasture with irrigated meadows that produce hay for winter grazing. Here land cost per unit is $100 less. However, irrigation is a new factor for which labor and equipment cost at least $8 per head. Blizzard risk is substantial and custom workers and commercial truckers are not readily available causing ranchers to maintain their own equipment. Because of such factors and the increased complications of operation, an owner needs a much larger facility to sustain high calibre management; a bigger and more specialized staff; and a considerably greater investment in equipment. Example: If you are 100 miles from a repair garage or shop during the haying season and a tractor breaks down, you need a supply of spare parts and a man who can perform as a mechanic.

As a final example, let us use Florida in the Belle Glade area. In this country two acres of improved land can support a cow. Properly improved, drained, and seeded areas cost $250 per acre and there is no winter feeding. Calf crops should average 90% and one bull should be able to handle 20% more cows than in Wyoming. On the other hand, tremendous quantities of fertilizer have to be constantly put on the fields or the grass has no substance and the cattle don't gain, and it is still possible to have a disaster like the winter of 1957-58 where the frost killed off most of the tropical type grass.

In summary, while each cattleman is absolutely convinced that his own country is the best, a closer look reveals that one item balances another. When they don't, land values and rents rise or fall to bring the total back into adjustment.

4. MATHEMATICAL CONCLUSIONS AND THE FUTURE

Taking a short term look at things, and if the preceding paragraph proves true, there will always be rapid short term adjustments. However, some long term trends have set in which, barring radical government action, are mathematical certainties. The pattern started with the collapse of the cattle market in 1953 and the three years of severe drought which followed. This shook up existing ownership and established procedures to such an extent that it triggered developments which were inevitable but might have been postponed another 20 years. In the first place, it drove the marginal farmer and rancher out of business and forced him to sell his property or give up his leases. Second, it left many of the remaining operators undercapitalized to the point that they are unable to take advantage of the new equipment and techniques that are about to hit the market. On the other hand, it permitted the stronger operator to assemble land that he would not otherwise have been able to acquire.

Let us go back to the arithmetic of the Kansas ranch used in the first section. Let us assume that 9,000 acres were assembled instead of 3,000 and that you now have a 1,500 cow ranch instead of 500 cows:

1. You can hire a top manager for $10,000 instead of three at $6,000. (Saving $5.33/head.)
2. With two men at $4,000 and temporary help totalling $3,000 he can do a good job. (Saving $4.66/head.)
3. By mass carload purchasing, better equipment and better utilization of own cultivated land the item of "feed" can be reduced $2 per head.
4. Equipment costs can be reduced 30% or $4 per head. (Example: One 2-1/2 ton truck with automatic dispenser can feed more cottonseed cake with one driver than three 1/2 ton pickups and

three drivers. In addition, the feed can be handled in bulk saving $4 per ton in sacking and all the extra labor of handling the sacks.)

These items come to a total of $16 in savings per head or an increase of 700% in net operating profit. No consideration is given to the fact that the larger operator, when he sells, can force the buyers to come to him; avoid the commission and the shrink at the central markets; can sort into uniform carloads lots on shipment and can conservatively net out 1c per lb. better than the small operator. On a 400 lb. calf this is $4 per head.

The savings from the assemblage of land is only one phase of this revolution we are watching. The second and more significant phase is the end of cheap labor. There are no more $75 per month Mexicans in Texas; there are no more $100 per month itinerant irrigation workers in Montana; and there are no more experienced cattle managers who are willing to work 18 hours a day and who are capable of running a half million dollar investment in land and cattle, that can be hired at $350 per month.

All that has occurred over the last five years is important, but it is only setting the stage for what is known in scientific research as the "breakthrough." For 2,000 years people grazing cattle have put up hay, chopped weeds and brush out of their pastures, and bred their cow herds with bulls. The following are examples not of theories to be put in use in 1990, but of items that will be in general use by 1970. By that time, I am convinced that large, properly staffed ranches and farms will be:

1. Using the new automatic grass choppers and dehydrators which combine five operations in one. The present hay bale will be as obsolete as the former hay stack and no human hand will touch alfalfa from the time it grows in the field until the day a cow eats it from an automatic dispenser.
2. Spraying and reseeding by aircraft to replace ground operations in all but the flattest land.
3. Implanting fertilized ovum from $20,000 cows and bulls in $200 cows and within a five year period, putting 80% of existing cow herds in the same class as the Texas Longhorn.

5. SUMMARY

It's a tough job to operate a ranch of under 500 head capacity and make a small return on your investment. This automatically eliminates most of the land east of the Mississippi because land ownership is too split up to put that much together any more. In the range areas of the country, savings in one category of expense are matched by increases in others so everything pretty well evens out.

The market collapse and drought of the 1952-54 period triggered a movement into ranch and farm consolidation that would have happened anyway because of the tremendous savings accomplished with larger size. The disappearance of cheap labor has been another handicap to the small ranch and brought more emphasis on the new types of equipment which are only economical to the larger operations.

Scientific "breakthroughs" in agriculture and ranching over the *next* five years bear every indication that they will be as far reaching as the developments in nuclear physics and missiles have been over the *last* five years.

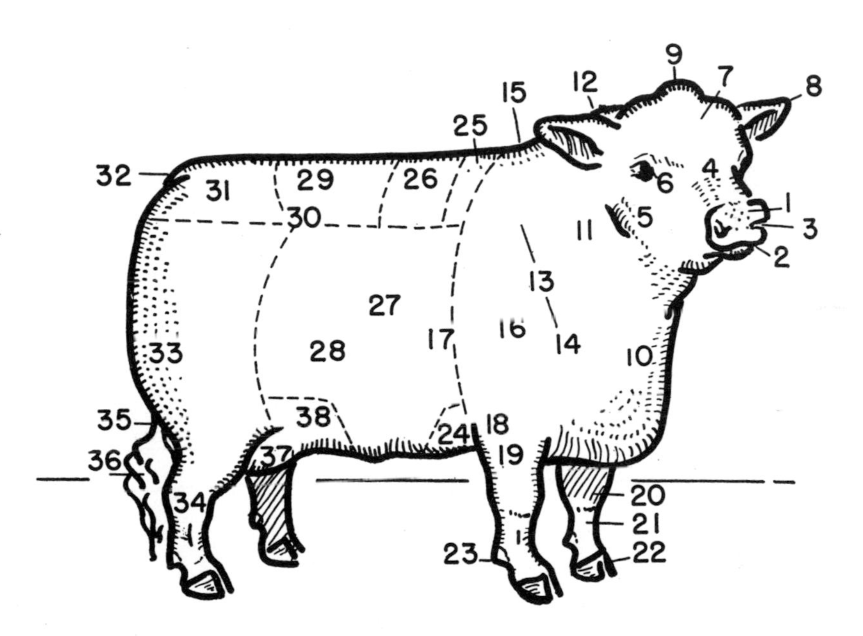

Parts of a steer. The first step in preparation for judging beef cattle consists in mastering the language that describes and locates the different parts of the animal. (Drawing by R. F. Johnson)

1. Muzzle
2. Mouth
3. Nostril
4. Face
5. Jaw
6. Eye
7. Forehead
8. Ear
9. Poll
10. Dewlap
11. Neck
12. Crest
13. Shoulder vein
14. Point of shoulder
15. Top of shoulder
16. Shoulder
17. Fore ribs or heart girth
18. Elbow
19. Arm
20. Knee
21. Shank
22. Foot
23. Dew claw
24. Fore flank
25. Crops
26. Back
27. Ribs
28. Belly
29. Loin
30. Hip or hook
31. Rump
32. Tail-head
33. Thigh
34. Hock
35. Tail
36. Switch
37. Cod
38. Rear flank

HANDY JUDGING GUIDE FOR BEEF CATTLE[1]

Procedure For Examining, And What To Look For	Ideal Type	Common Faults
Side View:		
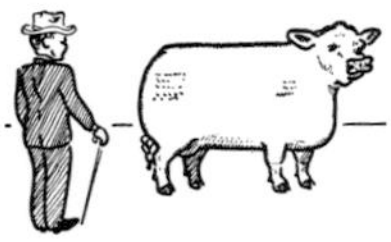 1. Size for age; know what they should weigh	 1. Large, early-maturing	 1. Undersized; too small
2. Balance and symmetry	2. Balanced and symmetrical	2. Lacking in balance and symmetry
3. Depth of body	3. Great depth of body throughout	3. Shallow bodied
4. Compactness	4. Short coupled	4. Long-bodied
5. Low-setness	5. Low-set	5. Leggy; upstanding
6. Straightness of top and bottom lines	6. Straight top and bottom lines	6. Easy in the back, and high in the flanks
7. Blockiness	7. Blocky	7. Angular
8. Depth of quarters	8. Deep, full quarters	8. Light in the quarters
9. Shortness of neck	9. A short, thick neck	9. Long necked
10. Fullness of crops	10. Full, thick crops	10. Slack in the crops
*11. Straightness of legs	11. Straight, true, and squarely set legs	11. Crooked legs; sickle hocked, cow hocked, too straight in the hocks, etc.
12. Size of bone	12. Ample bone, with quality (steers rather fine boned)	12. Coarse boned, lacking quality (or breeding animals too fine boned)
13. Quality and smoothness	13. Showing quality and smoothness	13. Rough or coarse; lacking in quality
14. Style	14. Plenty of style	14. Lacking in style
*15. Breed type (color, shape of body, and head and horn characteristics true to breed)	15. Showing plenty of breed type	15. Lacking breed type
Rear View:		
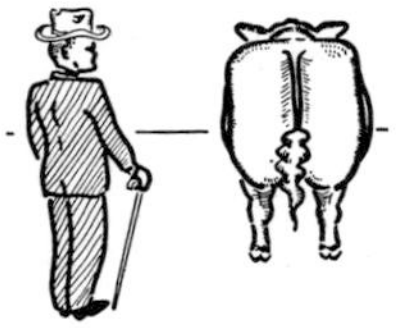 1. Uniformity of width from front to rear	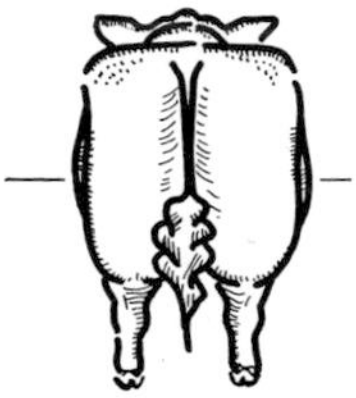 1. Uniformly wide from front to rear	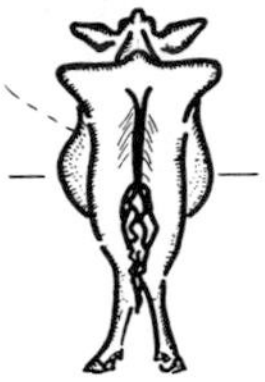 1. Narrow bodied
2. Width over the top	2. Wide over the top	2. Lacking width over the top
3. Trimness of middle	3. Trim in the middle	3. Paunchy
4. Levelness of rump	4. Level rump	4. Sloping in the rump
5. Width, depth, and fullness of quarters	5. Wide, deep, full quarters	5. Lacking width, depth, and fullness of quarters
*6. Set to hind legs	6. Legs set wide apart	6. Cow hocked.

[1]The illustrations for this table were prepared by R. F. Johnson.
*Not as important in fat steers as in breeding animals.

	Procedure For Examining, And What To Look For	Ideal Type	Common Faults
Front View:			
	*1. Shapeliness of head	1. A shapely head, with a short face, broad forehead, and wide muzzle	1. A plain head
	*2. Sex character	2. Cows show femininity; bulls show masculinity	2. Cows lacking femininity; bulls lacking masculinity
	3. Brisket	3. Wide, rounded, neat and trim	3. Too heavy and wasty in the brisket
	4. Width of chest	4. A wide chest	4. A narrow chest
	*5. Set to front legs	5. Correctly set front legs	5. Crooked front legs, or twisted (or curled) bones or feet
Handling:	1. Thickness and evenness of fleshing	1. Thickly and evenly fleshed	1. Patchy; uneven in covering; or lacking thickness of fleshing
	2. Quality of hide and mellowness	2. A loose, pliable, mellow hide	2. Coarse hided and hard
	†3. Finish	3. A fat, well-finished steer	3. Lacking finish, or overdone, soft and flabby

*Not as important in fat steers as in breeding animals.
†Not important in breeding animals.

When cattle are being trailed, the strongest and best are usually in the front and the weakest in the rear. (Courtesy, American Hereford Assn.)

Traders bidding for grain in the "pit" of the Kansas City Board of Trade. (Courtesy, Kansas State Board of Agriculture)

Chapter XIII

Market Play

At the present moment livestock may be the nearest to a "free market" of any item that is bought and sold in quantity in the United States. Common stocks and other securities are closely watched by the S. E. C. and the regulating bodies of the New York and the American Stock Exchanges. At the present moment the government prohibits you from buying on less than a high percentage margin. On most of the major grains the government price support program provides a floor, and government regulations closely control all the central markets. In many commodities, the day's trading is suspended by law if there is a market move over a given number of cents per bushel. Cattle are governed by the old laws of supply and demand with the Devil taking the hindmost.

While not nearly as important a factor as in the old days when cattle drives had to be accomplished on foot, the generally rather heavy expense of shipping live animals on the hoof permits a considerable price differential from a free market in one section of the country and that in another. More than the price differential is the loss in shrinkage and possible damage in health that an animal will suffer by being transported a thousand miles in a truck or freight car. This is the reason why after a localized drought in southern California that there is not a great flood of animals coming in from South Dakota. The movement can occur but the price differential between the two markets must be considerable to justify it.

This chapter will be divided into three sections:

1. The Mechanics of Marketing.
2. Differentials Between Geographic Markets.
3. Daily Market Play.

1. MECHANICS OF MARKETING

In the old days when all large cattle movements were by rail, cattle would come into a central market consigned to a commission house known and friendly to a given rancher. The commission house would sell either to a packing house, to a registered trader at the yards who would buy for his own account, or to feeders or other commission men who had been authorized to buy for their accounts.

The "traders" at the stockyards are normally men who would buy for their own accounts in rather large wholesale quantities and then sort and "shape" the herds for retail sales to the small farmers and feeders. Their average profits over a year would run from 25c to 50c per hundred pounds. Obviously, on some days, if they caught a rising market they could do very well; on other days they might take substantial losses.

The commission houses would take a commission on both the sale from the selling client, as well as from the purchasing client. All of these intermediate middleman charges would normally run from $2 to $5 per head on the overall transaction between seller and buyer.

The stockyards themselves make their profits from the rather high price of feed sold while the cattle are in the pens and various "yardage" fees. Other fees are charged the commission houses and the traders for the use of the pens which normally belong to the stockyards company and are rented out. In most cases the stockyards also own the central office building associated with the yards and charge rent to all of the users.

"Order buyers" could be commission men, traders, or regular salaried employees of associations or packing house groups who have been given firm orders to buy for their accounts a certain number of cattle at specified weights and grade. When the cattle are purchased, they are authorized to write drafts on the buyer's account. As a rule in most central yards, all of the above people are bonded.

Until about twenty years ago, probably about 80% of the cattle changing hands in the United States followed a pattern something similar to the above. The big change in all of this was occasioned by the development of the trucking industry and the large national highways. This caused the rise of the "Country Auction." In this situation, usually on a given day of the week, cattle over a given neighborhood are brought into a local sales barn and are auctioned off in various size lots by professional auctioneers. A fee is paid on a per head basis to the auction house and usually additional profit is made by the auction house from the sale of hay and feed on which they have a monopoly.

At these auctions, the seller is permitted to put in a bid and buy back his cattle if he feels that he is not getting the proper price. In some cases the auctioneer has been directed by the seller to "take a bid off the back of the tent" if he doesn't feel that there is enough action and if the cattle are going to be "given away." In recent years these auctions have acquired enough volume that direct representatives of the major packing houses usually attend them and buy for their own firm's account, and traders and order buyers come in from the major feeders so as to completely circumvent the central markets.

Many of these markets are located in areas not serviced by railroads and cattle come in by truck and go out by truck.

For a considerable amount of history, most of the registered pedigreed business was conducted by "private treaty." This is where the buyer and seller directly meet and work out a price without an intervening agent. In recent years with the return of the large-scale operation, particularly as regards feeders, many of the major feed operators in Missouri, Iowa, and Illinois send their own salaried employees directly into the ranch country to contract for the delivery of large quantities of a given class of animal to be weighed off of the ranch under certain conditions three, four, six and even as much as eight months ahead of time. It is customary to put up $5 or $10 per head as earnest money on these contracts and to go into great detail as to the conditions of weighing; whether or not the cattle are to be watered or fed on the day of weighing; who is responsible for the truck bills to the scales; how the cattle are to be worked before and during the day of weighing; and what treatment should be given to any cattle that don't come up to "normal specifications" or are "unmerchantable."

"Shrink" is the amount of actual weight that an animal will lose while it is being jostled around the pens, driven to the scales, or trucked to the nearest public scales. In some cases where the weighing conditions are extremely favorable to the seller and the cattle are not going to actually receive much "physical shrink," the buyer often demands that 2% or 3% be subtracted from the final weight of the cattle to compensate him for these unfavorable weighing conditions. This is known as a "pencil shrink."

The annual net profit of many a cattle trader is based on "shrink." If a 700 pound yearling steer was shipped 600 miles from a grass pasture in Oklahoma on a hot August day after it had been jostled around in a corral and the trucker had overcrowded it and took two days in the drive, it could have shrunk 50 pounds or 7% on arrival at a Kansas City scale. At 30c per pound, this is worth $15.

It will recover half of this weight after it has been fed, watered and rested. However, it will take ten days on pasture to fully recover the initial weight. Newly weaned calves might take three weeks to start eating and recover initial weights. 800 pound steers off of a grain feed, shipped on a cold day and carefully handled, might only shrink 2% or 16 pounds.

A trader who buys shrunk out animals, even at a premium, puts them in a feed lot near the yards for a week, and sells them at a 1c/lb. discount will still make a profit from the shrink recovery. Often, with the improvement in appearance from a rest and a "fill," he won't have to give a price discount and can make the full shrink recovery.

In connection with this increasing volume of sales by "private treaty" or by "future delivery contract," a new class of middleman has arisen known as the "contract trader." There are probably fifty to a hundred such individuals in the United States who may be individually doing over $2,000,000 per year in volume. They are the ones who in the spring of the year will contract large volumes of cattle from the ranchers and then proceed to sell these "fall delivery contracts" to feeders, packing houses, or other ranchers, depending on which way the market goes between spring and fall.

Because no single herd of cattle is exactly like another herd despite all of the government regulations on grading, a buyer will rarely agree to take a fall delivery contract unless a specific herd and a given brand is pinned down in the contract. If he uses normal business judgment, he will actually have someone make a physical inspection of the herd before he signs the contract with the trader. Consequently, the business of "short selling" done with common stocks and with many of the grain commodities is very unusual.

On occasion a buyer will make an arrangement with a trader with whom he has done previous business and in whom he has implicit confidence to take "1,000 steer yearlings guaranteed choice and not to weigh over 1,000 pounds on an October 15 delivery at 30c per pound." The trader might not have these animals and would be in a "short" position. He would then have to go out and locate these animals at a later date to cover his "short" contract. I would be willing to wager, however, that transactions of this sort make up less than one-half of one per cent of the annual volume of American cattle trades. The principal problem here is that two ranchers might both have a herd that would technically (and with some argument) grade out "choice." However, one rancher's herd might be uneven in weight and size over the others. Likewise, one rancher might have a herd of proven genetic background and a quality of breeding that would produce much greater results in the feed lot than the others. The area of the country they came from, the way they have been fed and treated the last month or two before sale, and a dozen other factors could influence the price at which they would finally go. All of these are reasons why "short sales" are almost unknown. One thousand head of cattle are a totally different commodity from 1,000 shares of General Motors stock.

2. GEOGRAPHIC DIFFERENTIAL

On a given day due to local weather conditions preventing buyers or sellers from arriving, it would not be at all unusual for there to be a 2c per pound differential on prices between Kansas City, Omaha, Denver, Sioux City, and Chicago. This could amount to as much as 10% or 15% of the selling price of the animal. It would be unlikely that anything greater than this would persist because it would then become economically worthwhile to physically move animals from one area to another.

Beyond the daily fluctuation due to local conditions, the general trend is that the closer you are to big centers of consumption, such as New York, Chicago and Los Angeles, that prices ought to be higher by at least the amount of the transportation. A country auction in a small town on the northern border of western Montana should certainly average out $5 to $10 per head cheaper than the Kansas City market. However, even this is not an absolute rule. For example, if this section of Montana had droughts for a couple of years and the greater part of the herds had been liquidated, the ranchers would start to restock their ranges after a rain came. In this case, they could very well pay over Kansas City prices locally to get cattle moved in from more distant areas. During 1957 and 1958 this specific situation existed in northern Texas, Oklahoma, Arizona and New Mexico after the great droughts of 1953, 1954, and 1955.

As an example of the variation among the big mid-western markets, we have reprinted a chart from the May 17, 1960, Department of Agriculture report:

STOCKER AND FEEDER CATTLE: AVERAGE COST, WEIGHT, AND NUMBER

Add "000's" to all figures

	Week Ended			*Month*		*Four Months*	
	May 12 1960	*May 5 1960*	*May 14 1959*	*Apr. 1960*	*Apr. 1959*	*Jan.–Apr. 1960*	*Jan.–Apr. 1959*
Steers–							
1001# up	687	869	871	3,104	4,632	11,568	20,815
901-1000	1,865	1,872	1,821	8,485	11,944	35,805	42,385
801-900	3,115	3,744	3,258	11,811	16,270	54,060	59,176
701-800	4,270	4,545	4,915	17,654	22,548	67,561	72,598
501-700	13,296	14,214	9,110	50,937	57,595	160,519	177,584
Total steers– 10 markets	23,233	25,244	19,975	91,991	112,989	329,513	372,558
Av. wts. steers– 10 markets	703#	705#	726#	708#	721#	724#	731#
Av. cost* steers– 10 markets	$24.74	$25.02	$28.72	$25.30	$28.48	$24.50	$27.63
Chicago	25.10	24.60	28.79	24.40	28.21	24.14	26.75
Kansas City	25.61	25.82	29.09	25.46	28.63	24.51	27.31
Omaha	25.45	25.13	29.21	25.48	29.57	24.52	28.33
S. St. Paul	23.53	23.39	26.70	23.83	26.10	23.23	25.28
Sioux City	26.07	26.18	30.19	26.38	29.89	25.71	29.45
Denver	25.38	24.76	28.08	25.74	28.01	25.05	28.25
Ft. Worth	20.85	22.47	27.48	24.18	27.59	23.82	27.45
Oklahoma City	23.13	23.78	27.40	24.13	26.87	23.41	26.54
S. St. Joseph	24.68	25.37	28.42	25.05	27.86	24.20	27.07
St. Louis NSY	24.70	24.46	27.12	24.45	27.29	23.66	26.27
Total calves– 10 markets	6,198	6,515	7,689	33,808	30,904	148,122	146,612
Total heifers– 10 markets	3,316	3,876	4,098	15,838	22,880	50,435	69,125
Total cows– 10 markets	466	391	587	1,657	2,736	10,689	13,089

*Not adjusted for differences in grade of cattle sold at each market.

Totally unrelated to any of the above is a separate phenomenon due to seasonal variations between one section of the country and another. For example, in California rains start in September and the good cheap grass conditions occur during the "winter." June, July and August are the months of dry pasture, drought, and the feeding of expensive hay. Consequently, it is customary to breed cows to drop their calves in September and to be prepared to wean them off and sell all yearlings by June of the following year when the heavy expenses start.

In areas of spring rains and good summer pastures but cold winters and heavy winter feeding expenses, the cycle is just the opposite. All of this means you have your heavy season of marketing coming at different times of the year in different areas. An additional problem is a difference in terms and grade even among field men of the Department of Agriculture Grading Service. Traditionally an animal that would be called "low choice" in Los Angeles would be lucky to make "medium good" in Omaha. A "calf" in Missouri could be a 14-month 600 pounder. This could be a "late yearling" in Texas and a "coming two" in South Dakota.

Beyond this, you have the physical factor that cattle from widely different geographic areas might take as much as one year to adapt themselves to new climatic conditions before starting to put on the normal growth. This acts as somewhat of a bar to free movement between widely separated areas regardless of the transportation costs. For example, it would probably be an extremely bad practice to move cattle from South Dakota to Florida even if the transportation were for free.

3. DAILY MARKET PLAY

At the time in which this book is being written, the Dow-Jones industrial average on the common stock market has been fluctuating near the lower 600 level. A 5% change at this level during a single day would be 30 points and would mean headlines in every newspaper in the world. A 5% change in the price of cattle at either the central markets, the country auctions, or on future contracts is a daily occurrence that hardly occasions the lifting of an eyebrow. In fact, on the same day it is quite possible for prices in South Dakota to go up 5% and prices in northern Arizona to go down 5%, again without more than a passing glance from the industry.

It is obvious that this type of wide daily fluctuation is a matter of almost routine, and that considerable money can be made or lost by traders and speculators who buy and sell for their own account within a forty-eight hour period.

One of the principal fortunes in the cattle business has been made by a man whom we shall anonymously call Mr. Tom Smith, on a very simple device. Mr. Smith owns one of the large trading houses in one of the principal stockyards and is also in partnership with several of the major ranchers and feed lots at distances running from 100 to 300 miles from the location of the stockyards.

For years he has cultivated the friendship of the freight agents of the principal railroads serving his city. Every Friday night he has been in the habit of calling them to find out what cattle shipments are scheduled to arrive at his stockyards on the following Monday morning. He finds out what major class of cattle is coming in, what their weights are, and what their general quality and condition is.

If it looks like 1,000-pound two year old steers are going to arrive in volume, he directs all of his own people to hold off shipping anything in this category. If at the same time nothing substantial is coming in on dry utility cows, that is the moment that he sells the drys which he already had sorted off in special close-in pastures for just this kind of play. On annual sales in excess of $10,000,000, this freight agent intelligence system could not have failed to give him an increase of 3% in his annual net which would amount to around $300,000 per year. Besides this, he has built up a substantial customer clientele who know that he always has the particular class of cattle in his pens on which the market seems to be short that day.

Chapter XIV

Prices and Cycles

Prices of cattle, like any other basic commodity, are a function of the old law of supply and demand. "Demand" varies with the class of cattle you are talking about. Sides of beef go to the retailers. Fat cattle go to the packing houses. Feeders go to the grain farmers. Breeding stock goes to the ranchers.

On a long term basis the ultimate consumption of beef by the American public will govern all classes of "demand." However, on a short term basis there can be radical fluctuation within the classes of "demand." For example, there could be simultaneously a poor demand for choice two year old steers by the packers and a great demand for young range cows by the ranchers.

Supply or quantities available for marketing, crossing the curve of demand, determines price. These types of fluctuations in cattle adhere to certain historical and traditional patterns. Anyone who could predict them with complete accuracy would be many times a millionaire and there aren't too many of these persons in the cattle business. The patterns of price fluctuations can be divided into three categories: weekly, seasonal, and annual.

Weekly movements in the old days were completely tied in with the railroads and the big city central markets. With the increasing prominence of the trucking industry and the country auctions, this is in a state of flux.

In the old days the big packing houses were all in large cities such as Chicago, Omaha and Kansas City. They bought only from their own central stockyards. The only cheap way to the stockyards was by rail.

On a long rail haul, it was traditional to try to get your cattle to the yard pens Saturday and Sunday to give the cattle a day's rest and a chance to feed and water before the week started. With the greatest selection available on Monday morning, that became the traditional day for the majority of the buyers to congregate. A social element also entered the picture as the ranchers and farmers got into the habit of coming in Monday to meet their friends whether or not they really wanted to buy anything.

Gradually as volume increased, a considerable number of people tried to market on Tuesday figuring they might do better when all the rush was over. Generally, because of this pattern, the cattle still left by Wednesday and the balance of the week are considered "left overs" and will bring less money. The exception to this is culled cows who are bought by the packers with the price staying constant through Friday.

With cattle trucks now being able to pick up directly at the ranch, eliminating the need for a drive to the railhead, the country auction has come to the fore. The weekly one-day auction at Valentine, Nebraska, might exceed the volume of a central market. Recently the packing houses have been sending buyers to the country auctions which has given them a real shot in the arm. The local auction can be held Wednesday, Thursday or Friday and is gradually breaking up the historical weekly cycle.

Speculating on seasonal fluctuations is where many fortunes have been won or lost.

Generally, over 80% of the U.S. cows are bred in the early summer to drop calves in April. The calves are weaned in October or November and shipped to market. Simultaneously, people who carried over yearlings for one more year of grass ship when the season ends and winter feeding is about to start. The cost of keeping an animal is about three times for a winter month what it is for a summer month.

On the other hand, the grain farmer or feeder has completed his harvest by December but his hay or grain is in relatively cheap storage and he can afford to bide his time on purchasing feeders to catch the right market play. He is under some pressure as interest and storage charges can't be completely overlooked, and he doesn't want to wait too long and run the risk of carrying surplus feed over the next crop season. The government price support program and the CCC loan plan have taken much of the risk out of this as far as the grain producer is concerned.

In any case the increased flow to market *generally* results in a 2c to 3c drop per pound from the same animal in April and its identical twin in October. Likewise, a cow about to calve in April should be worth $25 more than the same animal who has just had a calf weaned off in November.

However, in one year out of four something seems to happen to reverse this seasonal cycle and the ranchers and feeders who out-guess the majority make big money.

Annual price fluctuations in cattle have intrigued experts for years. Tradition refers to a "seven year cycle." If this were exact and regular, no one would go broke and plenty do.

In a general way cattle go up and down with radical long term moves of the economy such as 1928-29 as opposed to 1931-33. Also in a general way the total numbers of cattle relative to the general population are significant.

The following charts are reprinted from the U. S. Department of Agriculture report of March 1960.

NUMBER OF LIVESTOCK ON FARMS AND RANCHES JANUARY 1, UNITED STATES, 1951 TO 1960

Year	*Number on Farms January 1*	*Index Numbers, by Groups (1947-49 = 100)*	
	All Cattle and Calves	*Meat Animals*	*Milk Cattle*
	1,000 head		
1951	82,083	105	96
1952	88,072	110	95
1953	94,241	112	97
1954	95,679	111	98
1955	96,592	114	96
1956	96,804	115	95
1957	94,502	112	93
1958	93,350	111	91
1959	96,650	116	88
1960*	101,520	120	88

*Preliminary.

NUMBER OF CATTLE AND CALVES ON FARMS AND RANCHES JANUARY 1, BY CLASSES, UNITED STATES, 1951 TO 1960

Year	*Not for Milk*				
	Cows & Heifers 2 yrs. & over	*Heifers, 1 to 2 yrs. old*	*Calves*	*Steers*	*Bulls*
	1,000 head	*1,000 head*	*1,000 head*	*1,000 head*	*1,000 head*
1951	18,526	5,122	14,319	7,029	1,689
1952	20,863	5,971	15,829	8,400	1,774
1953	23,291	6,535	17,440	9,147	1,907
1954	25,050	6,365	17,978	8,229	1,896
1955	25,659	6,514	18,785	8,444	1,829
1956	25,516	6,238	18,979	9,560	1,774
1957	24,754	6,017	18,621	9,105	1,735
1958	24,287	6,063	18,491	9,448	1,648
1959	25,513	6,820	19,698	10,233	1,651
1960*	27,263	7,419	21,093	11,009	1,752

*Preliminary.

FIRST MONDAY OF OCTOBER*

Year	*Choice Heifers 500-750 lbs.*	*Good & Choice Hfr. Calves 300-500 lbs.*	*Cows*
1949	$20.50-$23.00	$21.00-$25.50	$13.50-$16.00
1950	27.50- 29.00	27.00- 33.00	19.00- 22.00
1951	32.50- 36.50	31.00- 40.00	21.50- 25.50
1952	24.00- 26.00	21.00- 29.00	13.50- 17.00
1953	14.50- 16.50	11.50- 16.00	8.00- 10.50
1954	16.50- 18.50	15.50- 18.50	7.50- 10.00
1955	17.00- 19.00	15.50- 19.00	9.00- 10.50
1956	16.00- 18.00	14.00- 19.00	8.50- 10.50
1957	19.00- 21.50	18.00- 23.00	12.00- 14.50
1958	24.00- 29.50	25.00- 33.00	17.00- 21.00

*USDA reports from Kansas City Stockyards taken from respective issues of *Kansas City Star.*

Long range changes in eating habits of the public are significant. The switch from pork to beef in the last few years has been startling. The average consumption per year of beef has gone up from 53 pounds per person in 1952 to 82 pounds in 1959. The fashion and medical emphasis on being slim has caused the housewife to switch from the fatty cuts of prime to the lean cuts of high good.

One big national chain of grocery stores recently experimented by displaying prime, choice and good cuts at the same price per pound. The housewives picked the good three times out of four.

This change has had a big effect. Prime 3½ year old steers were once a significant part of the market. Now they are practically non-existent. By marketing animals at 18 months to 2 years at 40% less weight means that you need more breeding stock to keep up the same flow of total beef poundage in additional but smaller and younger slaughter animals.

To digress for a minute, the diet conscious housewife who wants less fat and more lean, eventually makes the power of her pocketbook felt all the way back the line to the master breeders.

Over the last 25 years the principal winners in the show ring have been the smaller "compressed smooth" types which were believed to more easily feed out to prime grade. While actually not proven, it is felt that extreme efforts of the registered breeders in this regard unfortunately produced the widespread mutation of Dwarfism which has plagued many of the most famous pedigrees.

Aside from this, the commercial ranchers who keep one eye cocked on the grocery counter now want the larger more rugged primitive type bull. The progeny may not grade out as easily to prime but they are bigger with more but leaner meat. This may partly account for the recent popularity of imported British stock which is more akin to the original ancestral stock and, incidentally, has never developed Dwarfism.

Other significant and general factors on cattle prices are the 2 to 3% annual population increase; the recent inflationary history of a 2% decline in the dollar; and the gradual increase in production costs including the interest rates on cattle bank loans.

Sharp one or two year swings are almost always associated with distress liquidation due to widespread drought. The sharp following upswing is due to the need to restock the denuded pastures and ranges once the rains come.

Imports and exports of animals have been given wide publicity but they rarely amount to more than 1 or 2%.

In summary, annual price moves are associated with the following:

1. Total cattle numbers.
2. Total human population.
3. Beef consumption per person.
4. General health of the economy.
5. Class and weight of animals being slaughtered.
6. Drought or restocking after drought.
7. Devaluation of the dollar.
8. Imports (minor).
9. Government actions. (To date these have been negligible as far as cattle are concerned.)

Chapter XV

Cattle Financing

Loans using cattle and feed as security are historically as old as the country itself, and up until the last fifty years were the main form of commercial paper for 90% of the banks west of the Mississippi. Possibly because of this long background and tradition, many of the oldest and most conservative banks take chances on cattle paper that they wouldn't think of doing on most other forms of collateral.

Cattle as security for bank loans have these disadvantages:

1. They are mobile and great quantities can be loaded or unloaded in trucks in a short period of time.
2. Banks east of the Mississippi do not insist on brands which means that without them it is impossible to identify their security.
3. Banks do not insist on mortality insurance where they wouldn't think of loaning on a building without fire insurance.
4. Cattle are extremely volatile in price and a 30% fluctuation in a month is not unheard of.
5. By lack of water, pasture, or feed, cattle can deteriorate 20% in a few weeks.
6. On the big western ranges, it is impossible for a loan inspector to check the security unless he wants to spend several weeks with a full team of assistants.

Despite all of these points, in 1951 at one of the all time peaks in the cattle market, many banks were loaning up to 90% of the value of the herds where the owners were operating on leased lands and had practically no assets beside the cattle herds. A number of banks got badly burned and, as usual, they reversed the situation and refused to loan over 50% of value on what became a very depressed market in 1953 and 1954.

In August of 1960 on herd loans over $50,000, large city banks were charging 6% interest. In country banks or on smaller loans, they were getting 7%.

Cattle loans are normally made on "the livestock plus their increase." If a herd of cows is borrowed on in the fall, they will have calves on the ground in five months, and at that time what started out as a highly exposed loan becomes a fairly safe one. Likewise, loans on a herd of calves become relatively safe after the calves have gained 200 pounds.

Where the loaning agencies feel that there is an inadequate margin of security on the mortgage, it is customary to put up the winter feed supply, farm machinery, etc. as additional collateral. In some cases in the note, provision is made to release certain items in the mortgage as soon as the cattle reach a certain weight average or when a certain percentage of the calf crop is on the ground.

West of the Mississippi, in addition to the usual description of the note, terms of repayment, interest, etc., most chattel mortgages on cattle have the following provisions:

1. The age, number, sex, breed and quality of the livestock.
2. A diagram of the brand, where on the hide it is located, the state it is registered in.
3. A legal description or identification of the ranch or farm, and a statement that the cattle covered in the recorded chattel mortgage cannot be moved without permission of the mortgagee.
4. A statement that if the collateral deteriorates in value through mismanagement, accident, disease, lack of feed, etc. that the note becomes due immediately.
5. A requirement that the cattle be gathered for inventory if requested by a loan inspector.
6. Acknowledgements necessary for recording in the county where cattle are located.

As mentioned earlier, cattle insurance is rarely required by banks because it is prohibitively expensive. At the present time, casualty insurance on accidents in transportation or from lightning, etc. is relatively inexpensive and is almost a national monopoly of the Hartford Accident and Indemnity Company of Hartford, Connecticut. When you throw in blizzard risk in the northern areas the policy becomes pretty expensive. When you throw in epidemic or death from any cause, the only one that will write it is Lloyd's of London and the current charge is a 3% premium based on a 3% deductible clause. In other words, on a hundred cows, you don't make any money until the seventh animal dies. Lloyd's limits this policy only to some states and will not insure the large herds on the big ranges.

Most cattle loans are handled through the small country banks who in turn discount some of their paper at the big city banks. I should

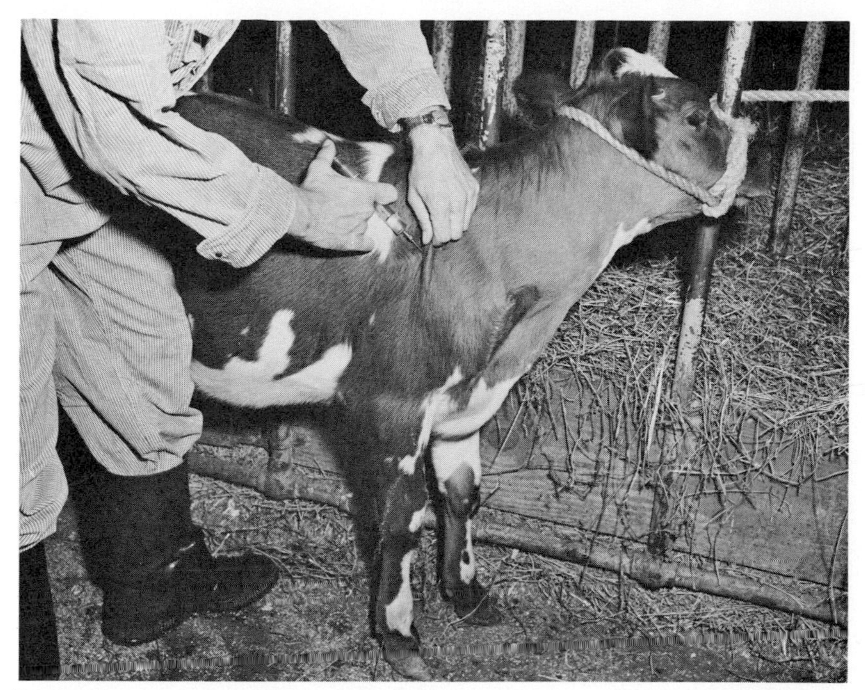

Veterinarian vaccinating calf against Brucellosis. This is one of the protection measures used in the Cooperative State-Federal Brucellosis Eradication Program of the U. S. Department of Agriculture. (Courtesy, the Office of Information, U. S. Department of Agriculture)

A cow suffering from Bang's (Brucellosis) has just aborted a dead calf. (Courtesy, the Office of Information, U. S. Department of Agriculture)

For Leptospirosis and Anaplasmosis or Brucellosis the only sure way of detection at the present time is by analyzing a blood sample. (Courtesy, the Office of Information, U. S. Department of Agriculture)

One of the cows in a Mexican dairy herd infected with foot-and-mouth disease. Salivation, caused by mouth ulcers, is one of the symptoms of the disease. (Courtesy, the Office of Information, U. S. Department of Agriculture)

Horses being gathered at a roundup in 1898. Note the XIT brand on the horse in the foreground. At that time it was extremely hazardous to have any animal in your possession not bearing your brand without a written bill of sale. (Courtesy, Rita Blanca Studio, Dalhart, Texas)

Choice and fancy spayed two-year-old heifers in the spring of 1958 off wheat pastures in transit to Iowa feedlots. Picture taken near Dalhart, Texas.

be extremely surprised if the major Chicago and New York banks had over ½ of 1% of their paper in direct cattle loans.

As a matter of interest, the following table shows the geographical variation in interest rates on livestock loans over eight states in country banks in the range areas. This information was derived from a survey of 152 country banks.

RATES FOR TYPICAL LIVESTOCK LOANS*

	Spring '56	*Spring '57*	*Spring '59*	*Spring '60*	*Possible Future*
Entire Area	A6.17%	6.40%	6.20%	6.54%	6.59%
	M6.00%	6.00%	6.00%	6.50%	6.50%
Colorado	A5.77%	6.10%	6.13%	6.34%	6.45%
	M6.00%	6.00%	6.00%	6.00%	6.50%
Kansas	A5.79%	6.03%	5.83%	6.21%	6.26%
	M6.00%	6.00%	6.00%	6.00%	6.00%
Missouri	A6.21%	6.33%	6.24%	6.42%	6.40%
	M6.00%	6.00%	6.00%	6.00%	6.00%
Nebraska	A——	——	5.83%	6.19%	6.28%
	M——	——	6.00%	6.00%	6.25%
New Mexico	A6.68%	6.75%	6.63%	6.94%	6.94%
	M6.75%	6.75%	6.50%	7.00%	7.00%
Oklahoma	A6.44%	6.70%	6.22%	6.75%	6.81%
	M6.00%	6.25%	6.00%	6.87%	7.00%
Texas	A6.24%	6.59%	6.70%	7.03%	7.03%
	M6.00%	6.75%	6.00%	7.00%	7.00%
Wyoming	A6.10%	6.25%	6.21%	6.75%	6.83%
	M6.00%	6.00%	6.00%	6.75%	7.00%

A—Average M—Median

*"Country Bank Loan Rate & Policy," Lloyd C. Riggs, Editor, *Bank News*, Kansas City, Missouri, May 15, 1960, p. 42.

These rates run about ½% less than the same groups of banks are making on other farm loans and are approximately ½% less than they were getting for livestock loans six months ago.

The Production Credit Associations are government sponsored agricultural loan cooperatives similar to the Federal Land Banks. They require the borrower to buy a small amount of stock at the time the loan is made. They generally loan about 1½% over prime New York interest rates.

In recent years a number of the large commission houses, feed companies, and independent packers have been extending credit to the rancher and feeder in order to better control his business. For some reason the large national finance companies have not gone into this field.

There are some individual state laws going back over one hundred vears peculiar to cattle mortgages. For example:

1. In some states a bank cannot foreclose on a herd mortgage without leaving enough cows "for a widow to provide milk for her family."
2. In some states an unpaid pasture bill provides a lien senior to a previously recorded chattel mortgage. In other states it is the reverse.

Chapter XVI

Growth and Cost Projections on a Breeding Herd

In these projections the following assumptions are made:

1. Cows are bred at 15 months to drop at two years.
2. An 80% calf crop percentage is maintained.
3. Annual maintenance on a cow, including breeding fees and management fees, but excluding mortgage interest, personal property taxes and depreciation, is calculated to average $80.
4. Annual maintenance on calves will average $50 and yearlings will average $60.
5. No mortality is figured.
6. No culling is figured except that all cows are sold off in their ninth year.
7. The primary cow herd is given a capital letter "A"; its first calf crop is labeled "A_1"; its second calf crop "A_2." As soon as a calf crop is old enough to drop calves, its designation is changed to a new letter, i.e., in the third year of operation described herein, "A_1" becomes "B" and the first crop of "B" is labeled "B_1."
8. The operator starts in November of 1960 and pays all of his expenses in that month through November of 1961. Each year he is then paid up one year in advance, with the result that in a year that he decides to sell his cattle business, he gets the herd growth of that year but has no expenses because they were paid at the end of the preceding year.
9. In these projections no consideration has been given to tax matters but it should be noted that the capital investment of hard dollars occurs only in the first year and is eventually converted into soft dollars by depreciation write-off. Consequently, no differentiation is made in the final liquidation as it is assumed that the original purchase has been depreciated to zero by that time. No consideration is given to salvage value.

10. Again no consideration is given to the fact that the hard dollar investment may be cut to 15% or 20% of the figures shown by chattel mortgage borrowing.

11. Bull calves are traded for heifer calves.

COW-SPRING CALF PROJECTION

1960:		*Cost*
A	100 three year old cows bought in November bred to drop calves in spring of 1961, at $240 each for capital investment of....	$24,000
	Maintenance for these 100 cows with their spring calf crop....	8,000
	Initial nonrepetitive first year expenses........................	3,000
	Total cash outlay 1960	$35,000

1961:		
A	100 cows	$ 8,000
A_1	80 calves	4,000
	Total 1961	$12,000

1962:		
A	100 cows	$ 8,000
A_1	80 yearlings	4,800
A_2	80 calves	4,000
	Total 1962	$16,800

1963:		
A	100 cows	$ 8,000
A_2	80 yearlings	4,800
A_3	80 calves	4,000
B	80 cows	6,400
B_1	64 calves	3,200
	Total 1963	$26,400

1964:		
A	100 cows	$ 8,000
A_3	80 yearlings	4,800
A_4	80 calves	4,000
B	80 cows	6,400
B_1	64 yearlings	3,840
B_2	64 calves	3,200
C	80 cows	6,400
C_1	64 calves	3,200
	Total 1964	$39,840

1965:

It is decided to liquidate the herd in the fall of 1965. All expenses on the herd for this year were paid in advance the preceding year.

No. of Animals in November		*Estimated Liquidating Value*	*Total*
A	100 cows (old)	$160.00	$16,000.00
A_4	80 yearlings	180.00	14,400.00
A_5	80 calves	120.00	9,600.00
B	80 cows	240.00	19,200.00
B_2	64 yearlings	170.00	11,520.00
B_3	64 calves	120.00	7,680.00
C	80 cows (threes)	240.00	19,200.00
C_1	64 yearlings	180.00	11,520.00
C_2	64 calves	120.00	7,680.00
D	80 cows (twos)	220.00	17,600.00
D_1	64 calves	120.00	7,680.00
B_1E	64 cows (twos)	220.00	14,080.00
B_1E_1	51 calves (great granddaughters of A)	120.00	6,120.00
	Total liquidating value of herd		$162,280.00
	Less 7% for culling, mortality and optimism		11,359.60
	Net liquidating value of herd		$150,920.40
	Total of expenses and investment 1960-65		$130,040.00
	Add 8% for contingencies		10,403,20
	Total cash outlay		$140,443.20
	Net liquidating value of operation		150,920.40
	Net gain over five year period		$ 10,477.20

COW-FALL CALF PROJECTION

In this case, the initial 100 cow purchase is on cows that are "springers" which will drop calves immediately after purchase in the fall of 1960. A good man selecting these animals should be accurate over 95% and a 90% calf crop should be a minimum on the first go around. In summary, the projection should be the same as the previous except for the following:

1. Big, dry cows about to drop calves will cost $25.00 more per head than the group in the previous projection for a total of $2,500.00 more capital investment.
2. Because winter feeding in the winter of 1960-61 will have to be done with a cow and nursing calf instead of a dry cow, add $10.00 to the winter feed bill for a total of $1,000.00.
3. Because the 1961 grazing season will end up with eating yearlings rather than just weaned calves, add $20.00 to the pasture bill for a total of $2,000.00.
4. However, about five (5) months are gained on the breeding cycle, which will more than recover the extra cost at the time of liquidation.
5. A certain amount of risk is run in this type of deal in parts of the country where there are severe winters and the first calf crop can get caught in a blizzard.

WEANED-CALF PROJECTION

1960:		*Cost*
A	100 six month old calves are purchased in the fall of 1960 at $120.00 each for a total of	$12,000
	Initial nonrepetitive expenses for first year	2,000
	1960 maintenance for 1961	5,000
	Total 1960 cash outlay	$19,000

1961:		
A	100 yearlings that could be bred for fall calves in 1961 in southern climates or for 1962 calves in the north	$ 6,000
	Total 1961	$ 6,000

1962:		
A	100 cows	$ 8,000
A_1	80 calves	4,000
	Total 1962	$12,000

1963:		
A	100 cows	$ 8,000
A_1	80 yearlings	4,800
A_2	80 calves	4,800
	Total 1963	$16,800

1964:		
A	100 cows	$ 8,000
A_2	80 yearlings	4,800
A_3	80 calves	4,000
B	80 cows	6,400
B_1	64 calves	3,200
	Total 1964	$26,400

1965:

Herd liquidation in fall of 1965. All expenses were paid the previous year.

	No. of Animals in November	*Estimated Liquidating Value*	*Total*
A	100 cows (fives)	$230.00	$ 23,000.00
A_3	80 yearlings	180.00	14,400.00
A_4	80 calves	120.00	9,600.00
B	80 cows (threes)	240.00	19,200.00
B_1	64 yearlings	180.00	11,520.00
B_2	64 calves	120.00	7,680.00
C	80 cows (twos)	220.00	17,600.00
C_1	64 calves	120.00	7,680.00
	Total liquidating value of herd		$110,680.00
	Less 7% for culling, mortality and optimism		7,747.60
	Net liquidating value		$102,932.40
	Total of expenses 1960-65		$ 80,200.00
	Add 8% for contingencies		6,416.00
	Total cash outlay		$ 86,616.00
	Net liquidating value		102,932.40
	Net gain over five year period		$ 16,316.40

UNWEANED-CALF PROJECTION

In this case, everything is similar to the Weaned-Calf Projection except that the calves are purchased right after birth in the spring of the year, your initial capital investment is only about $20.00 per animal, and you pay out $50.00 to "lease" the nursing cow and rent pasture for the end of the weaning period. Essential differences are:

1. You have expensed out most of your capital investment the first year, but you do not have much of a depreciation base for future years.
2. There is a certain increased element of risk in that your animals are subject to the various calf epidemics during this period.
3. You may be picking up a number of inferior animals as it is hard to select them at this age, and the cows may not be able to nurse them properly.
4. On the other hand, you may be able to make much better deals with the owners insofar as these are the same risks they must run.

NARROW EQUITY WEANED-CALF PROJECTION WITH NORMAL CULLING

1. 100 weaned calves are purchased for 10% down and a 90% mortgage at 7% interest in advance.
2. Every year 10% of the herd is culled at prices about 25% less than normal for good animals and the proceeds are applied against the mortgage.
3. The mortgage is also reduced by a principal payment roughly equal to the amount of anticipated depreciation.
4. Personal property taxes and a contingency factor have been thrown into annual costs rather than at the end of the five years.
5. The annual culling factor eliminates undesirable animals and gives better liquidating value. It also would have the effect of increasing calf crop percentage and weight, which is not considered here.
6. On liquidation it is assumed that about a 7% premium can be acquired by offering two-year financing terms.
7. This same premium was paid on the original acquisition to get financing terms at the time of purchase.
8. The 100 Weaned-Calf Projection showing a narrow equity purchase was prepared at a slightly different price level. Further, the annual interest charges on the mortgage have somewhat increased operating costs.
9. No consideration has been given to a small maintenance premium

that might be necessary in the early days of the loan to get a rancher to guarantee a non-recourse note or to furnish the 90% financing himself. Generally, by the end of the second year the mortgage has been paid down sufficiently and the collateral has increased enough that this extra cost can be eliminated.

10. In the example, no consideration has been given to the alternative of taking "Declining Balance" or "Sum of the Digits" depreciation, if it is desired to go one of those routes.

100 WEANED-CALF PROJECTION

	Nov.'59	*Nov.'60*	*Nov.'61*	*Nov.'62*	*Nov.'63*	*Nov.'64*
(a) # of Cattle	100 calves @ $130 ea. for total— $13,000	90 yrlgs.	81 cows	73 cows 58 calves	66 cows 52 yrlgs. 52 calves	66 cows 52 cows 52 yrlgs. 52 calves
(b) # Culled	—	10 yrlgs.	9 cows	8 cows 7 calves	7 cows 6 yrlgs. 6 calves	—
(c) Equity or Principal	$ 1,300	$ 2,680	$ 2,844	$ 3,234	$ 2,942	—
Expenses (Maint., fees, interest)	7,100	5,760	6,561	8,826	10,840	—
(d) Proceeds from Culls	—	1,680	1,944	2,424	3,032	—
(e) Depreciation	—	1,000	900	810	730	$ 660
(f) Net Cash Requirement	8,400	6,760	7,461	9,636	10,840 —$90 = 10,750	—
Expense plus Depreciation	7,100	6,760	7,461	9,636	11,570	660
(g) Est. Gross Value of Herd After Culling	13,000	18,900	21,870	26,885	34,180	47,560
Remaining Bal. of Mtg.	11,700	9,020	6,176	2,942	—	—
(h) Net Value of Investment	1,300	9,880	15,694	23,943	34,180	47,560

TOTAL NET VALUE OF INVESTMENT	$47,560
TOTAL NET CASH REQUIREMENT	43,007
TOTAL ECONOMIC PROFIT	$ 4,553

EXPLANATION

(a) The calf crop is based on 80% of all animals exposed to breeding. Animals are bred between 16-20 months. (Gestation period is 9 months.)

(b) Culls computed at 10% per annum.

(c) Amortization computed at (1) proceeds from sale of culls plus (2) depreciation for year.

(d) Proceeds from culls computed at 20% less than market value of animals.

Estimated Value of Culled Animals

Calves	$104
Regular 12 month yearlings	152
Late 20 month yearlings	168
3 year old cows	216
4 year old cows	212
5 year old cows	200
6 year old cows	192
7 year old cows	176
8 year old cows	160

(e) Depreciation calculated at 12½% over $50 salvage value. No consideration has been given to two months' depreciation in 1959 and the 20% first year depreciation (on 20 M maximum permitted by Section 179 of 1958 law) not taken.

(f) Net cash requirements include expenses plus a portion (equal to amount of depreciation) of payments on the mortgage. Proceeds from culls at the end of the 4th year paid off the balance of the mortgage leaving $90 cash. This is deducted from net cash requirements.

(g) Values derived according to the following estimated market value of the herd based on March 1959 market prices:

Calves	$130
Yearlings (regular 12 month)	190
Yearlings (late 20 month)	210
3 year old cows	270
4 year old cows	265
5 year old cows	250
6 year old cows	240
7 year old cows	220
8 year old cows	200

(h) No consideration has been given to the following factors:

1. Each year approximately 5% additional calves will be derived from a standard practice of trading bull calves (which are more valuable than heifers) for a greater number of heifers. (50 bulls are traded for 53 heifers.)

2. Each year the largest and oldest 15% of the calf crop are customarily grouped and bred with the older animals of the preceding year. This practice has the net effect of adding an additional 5% to those animals available for liquidation at only a negligible increase in maintenance costs.

COMPARATIVE ANALYSIS

1. The most rapid way to get in a large, rounded breeding herd is with cows purchased just before they drop calves.
2. Here you get the faster depreciation on older animals as opposed to the slower write-off on young calves. (For tax information see Chapter X.)
3. The route for the least capital investment is with unweaned calves.
4. If there is a possibility that you will be forced to liquidate the herd the first year or two, the safest deal is the calf route, as the weight gain prior to maturity will just about recover your maintenance costs. In this case, you may be called a "feeder" and have to pay full income tax on the gain. (See Chapter X.)
5. As far as the banks are concerned, you can borrow out more money on calves, percentage-wise. The reason for this is that in the event of a foreclosure, it is necessary to find a particular buyer to get the most out of a good breeding herd while you can always get a twenty-four (24) hour sale on calves or yearlings at one of the big meat markets. In addition, there is more of an element of chance on the percentage of calves that a cow herd will produce than of the amount of weight gain heifer calves will put on during the course of the note and mortgage.
6. The good management of a cow herd requires a lot more skill than managing calves and yearlings. If you are nervous about the capability of a given ranch or farm manager, you are better starting him off on the calf route so that you can get a year's observation on him before he tackles the management problems of the more complex herd.
7. You can normally expect a 2% higher mortality on young calves than older cows, particularly after they are into their second calves.

Chapter XVII

Newspapers and Market Reports

Approximately 40% of the financial page of the average western or mid-western newspaper is devoted to items directly affecting the cattle operator.

At each of the major central stockyards there is usually a reporter for the town's principal newspaper who writes a daily column on the local market. Prices are generally quoted in dollars per 100 pounds which numerically is identical to the cents per pound often used by the Department of Agriculture. An increase of $2 per 100 would be called a "strong" market. A $1 per 100 increase might be called "steady to higher." A "steady" or "firm" market might be a constant price with no hold-over of inventory, where buyers and sellers were matched. A $1 drop would be called "weak to lower."

In evaluating these kinds of reports, two factors should be considered. Like every other newsman, the livestock reporter is looking for the spectacular to hold the reader's interest. Second, the officers of the stockyard company and the principal commission houses are his personal friends and he will try to angle his column to bring more farmers and ranchers into his city rather than a competitive city or country auction.

At the big central markets on the following morning the Department of Agriculture publishes a price summary of the previous day's averages and grades. The following is reprinted from the *Kansas City Star* of June 20, 1960.

Slaughter Steers–	
Choice, 700-900 lbs.	$24.75 @ 27.25
Choice, 900-1,100 lbs.	25.25 @ 27.25
Choice, 1,100-1,300 lbs.	25.25 @ 27.25
Choice, 1,300-1,500 lbs.	25.00 @ 27.25
Good, 700-900 lbs.	22.50 @ 25.25
Good, 900-1,100 lbs.	22.25 @ 25.25
Good, 1,100-1,300 lbs.	22.00 @ 25.25
Standard, all weights	18.50 @ 22.50
Utility, all weights	16.75 @ 18.75
Slaughter Heifers–	
Choice, 700-900 lbs.	24.50 @ 26.50
Choice, 900-1,100 lbs.	24.50 @ 26.50

Good, 600-800 lbs.	21.50 @ 24.50
Good, 800-1,100 lbs.	21.50 @ 24.50
Standard, all weights	18.00 @ 22.00
Utility	16.50 @ 18.00
Slaughter Cows–	
Commercial	17.00 @ 19.50
Utility	15.25 @ 17.00
Cutter	14.25 @ 15.50
Canner	12.50 @ 14.50
Bulls–	
Commercial	18.50 @ 19.50
Utility	18.00 @ 19.50
Cutter	17.00 @ 18.00
Vealers–	
Choice	23.00 @ 26.00
Good	21.00 @ 23.00
Standard	17.00 @ 21.00
Other Slaughter Calves–	
Choice	21.00 @ 24.00
Good	20.00 @ 22.00
Standard	16.00 @ 20.00
Stocker and Feeder Steers–	
Choice, 500-800 lbs.	25.00 @ 28.50
Choice, 800-1,050 lbs.	24.00 @ 27.50
Good, 500-800 lbs.	23.00 @ 25.75
Good, 800-1,050 lbs.	22.50 @ 25.00
Medium, 500-1,000 lbs.	18.00 @ 23.00
Common, 500-900 lbs.	15.00 @ 18.50
Stock Heifers–	
Good and choice	22.50 @ 25.50
Medium	17.50 @ 22.50
Stock Cows–	
Medium and good	15.00 @ 17.50
Stock Steer Calves–	
Good and choice	24.00 @ 33.00
Medium	21.00 @ 25.00
Stock Heifer Calves–	
Good and choice	22.50 @ 28.00
Medium	19.00 @ 22.50

"Slaughter" cattle refers to those about to go to a packing house. "Commercial and utility" cows are big, heavy cows that are dry or barren and have not been nursing a calf. Their carcasses will grade out good or low choice. "Canners and cutters" are thin, aged or diseased cows that will go into canned meat. If they are extremely bad the government inspectors will "condemn" them and they will go to a rendering plant. "Vealers" tend to be crossbred calves of a dairy herd weighing 60 to 150 pounds. "Bulls" are usually aged animals or something unfit for breeding purposes; they will go into sausage. The "stock cow" category at a central market is usually culls from a breeding herd that a small farmer might try to fatten for a year, get one calf, and then ship to the packers.

If you were a large rancher and were nervous about the cost of all feed going up substantially in December, you could protect yourself by a "hedging" operation. You could buy No. 2 yellow corn to be delivered in Chicago in the month of December at a price between $1.12¾ and $1.11½ (see following table for June 22). In the event all of the feed prices went up substantially, this corn contract would go also, and when you sold your Chicago corn contract the profit that you would make on it would probably compensate you for the additional cost of grain or other feed that you might have to buy on the cash market in Nebraska. It would be extremely unusual if it were profitable to you to actually take delivery on the corn in Chicago and have to pay the 20c or more per bushel shipping cost to actually have it physically delivered to you in Nebraska. Generally corn in Nebraska would run 25c per bushel cheaper than corn in Chicago.

On cash markets for major protein feeds it is common to specify the percentage of protein, the process by which it is obtained, whether or not the price is in bulk carloads, and whether it is sacked or pelletized. In the event it is sacked, one normally assumes it is in 100 pound sacks unless it is specified otherwise. Prices on these commodities are normally quoted in one ton lots by carload. Dehydrated alfalfa meal normally gives a minimum guarantee on vitamin A units. The hay market quotations usually specify whether it is alfalfa, prairie hay or some other type. The grade of hay on alfalfa is normally determined as to how many weeds it has in it, how stemmy it is, and what the protein content is. Brokerage houses making quotations on soybean meal or soybean pellets usually imply receipt at Decatur, Illinois with freight calculated from that point. On cottonseed products the market at Memphis, Tennessee is usually quoted with freight calculated from that point.

When a carload of grain hits a given central market, an actual sample of the grain is taken out of the carload, put in a tray and is available for physical inspection on the floor in the Board of Trade in the city concerned.

Continuing our newspaper reports, most grain and feed prices are quoted on either a "futures" market or a "cash" market. The cash market is what they would be sold for at the close of trading on that specific day delivered to a specific point. The futures market is the contract price at which reputable registered traders will commit themselves to buy or sell in a given future month paying freight costs to a given point.

Certain traditional patterns of grade classification and pricing are common to each industry and are implied when one reads the market quotations in the newspaper. For example, when you look at corn futures contracts the price is quoted in dollars and cents per bushel and while it refers only to corn it is understood that it means No. 2 yellow field corn which is the one most commonly used for feed in this country. The grade of a given grain is determined by the amount of its moisture content, the amount of extraneous weed and other seed or foreign matter in the grain, the general size, quality, age, and chemical composition.

The following futures table was published at the close of business on Wednesday, June 22, 1960 in the *Kansas City Star:*

KANSAS CITY

			Closed	
WHEAT–	High	Low	Wednesday	Tuesday
July	184⅞	184¼	184⅜	184¾
Sept.	188	187¼	187¼	187¾
Dec.	192¼	191¾	191¾	192⅛
Mar.	195¾	195⅜	195½	195½
GRAIN SORGHUMS–				
July	——	——	157¼	157¼

Opening prices in grain futures in Kansas City were: Wheat–July, 184½; September, 187½; December, 192½; March, 195⅜.

CHICAGO

WHEAT–				
July	182¾	182⅛	182⅛	182⅝-½
Sept.	185⅞	185¼	185¼-⅜	185¾
Dec.	192⅜	191½	191½	192¼-⅜
Mar.	195¾	195¼	195¼	195⅝
May	194⅞	194½	194⅝	194⅞
CORN–				
July	116¾	115¾	115⅞-¾	116⅞-¾
Sept.	116⅝	116	116⅛-¼	116⅝
Dec.	112¾	111½	111½	112¼-⅜
Mar.	116⅛	115⅛	115¼	116
May	117¾	117½	117½	118⅛

SOYBEANS–				
July	209½	208⅞	209⅛	209⅝-½
Sept.	209⅜	208¾	208⅞	209¼
Nov.	208	207¼	207¼	208
Jan.	211¾	211¼	211¼	211¾
Mar.	214¾	214⅛	214⅛	214⅞
RYE–				
July	118	117½	117⅞-⅛	118
Sept.	120¼	119⅝	119¾-⅞	120
Dec.	123½	122¾	122¾-⅞	123¼
Mar.	126	125⅜	125¾	125¾
May	125⅝	125½	125⅝	125¾
OATS–				
July	70	69⅝	69¾	70
Sept.	70¼	69⅞	70⅛	70⅜-¼
Dec.	73⅝	73¼	73⅜-½	73⅝
Mar.	75⅝	75⅛	75⅛	75⅝
May	——	——	75⅛	76⅛
SOYBEAN MEAL–				
July	54.10	53.85	53.95-54.10	54.05
Aug.	54.85	54.55	54.75-70	54.80
Sept.	53.65	53.45	53.35-45	53.60-70
Oct.	52.50	52.20	52.25-20	52.50
Dec.	52.60	52.35	52.30-35	52.65

The various market services reporting on the large movement of range cattle and future delivery contracts on range cattle generally get their information from the various country banks.

Very often you will see a phrase in the newspaper reports such as "three carloads arrived on a sold basis." This probably means that some rancher made a direct deal with a feeder but with an agreement that the cattle were to be delivered to a given central market by rail and the pay weights at the public scales at the market were to determine the price; after weighing the cattle, the freight cars were to be rerouted on to the feeder's city. Most stockyard companies require that such a type deal be routed through a regular commission house if the scales and the yard facilities are going to be used. "Warmed up" cattle generally refers to those that have been partially fed out and could go to the slaughter houses but are still thin enough that a feeder could make a further gain if he wanted to continue a feeding program. "Grass fat" cattle are those that come off of extremely good pasture such as the Kansas blue stem and are almost ready to go straight to a packing house without the intermediate stage of grain feeding. Generally the regular grain feed lot operators prefer to avoid this class of cattle as there is an initial loss of weight in the switchover from grass to grain.

Insofar as most of these contracts involve a future loan commitment from the bank, they are reasonably accurate. Such a report might read as follows:

> "Tom Smith of Valentine, Nebraska has contracted for 1,000 heifer calves from John Doe out of his herd on the Cheyenne reservation with a 10% cut, a 100 mile haul, and a dry overnight stand to be weighed in on the public scales at Sheridan, Wyoming on or about October 15th. The price was reported at 30c per pound."

U. S. Department of Agriculture reports and statistics are generally derived from the following sources: their own paid staff members physically present at the stockyards, the county agents operating under the extension divisions of the various state universities, individual questionnaires going to farmers and ranchers, shipment reports from the railroads and trucking companies, bank reports to the various federal reserve districts, and personal property counts of the various tax assessors in the rural areas. Generally the usual statistical tools of making a random sample and multiplying by so-called proven quantitative factors have been used.

Just as many of our national political polls have proven to be statistically unsound in the past, I am personally convinced that the radical changes that have occurred in the last ten years within the livestock industry may not have been accurately reflected in the department's techniques of getting information. As an example, I would like to site one specific phenomenon. The sudden population increase over the last fifteen years in states west of the Mississippi River caused a sudden and tremendous need for additional tax money to handle school district building programs. The school boards themselves put a sudden new pressure on local county assessors' offices to get more money. As a result, county assessors have refused to accept the former "paper estimates" of cattle owners as to the number of cattle they were running and have really cracked down, making physical numerical counts themselves, and imposing severe penalties on those who had formerly and chronically underestimated their inventory reports on the personal property tax return.

This trend has been particularly strong in counties which have recently received an influx of suburban or industrial population where political power has passed from the hands of the farmers and ranchers to the new school conscious residents.

I am personally convinced that at least 20% of the increase in cattle numbers that has occurred over the last fifteen years is due to more

From left to right, Mr. Barret S. Heddins, Jr., President, First National Bank of Kansas City; Mr. Rodney Moore, Cattle Inspector for Oppenheimer Industries, Inc.; and Mr. Harold Humphreys, Vice President in the Commercial and Livestock Loan Division. The First National Bank of Kansas City and the Interstate Bank with whom it merged in 1955 has been one of the major sources of cattle financing in the United States for three-quarters of a century.

President Theodore Roosevelt in his younger days on a western range. During his administration, the leasing of lands from the Public Domain was put on a fair and equitable basis and the rights of the homesteader were protected. (Courtesy, Library of Congress)

accurate reporting rather than an actual physical increase. A further factor in this direction has been the concentration of more of the agricultural and livestock industry in the hands of large well-staffed and better educated operators who actually fill out the questionnaires rather than throw them in the waste baskets as many of their predecessors did. Also, in the past the general feeling by the rural population that answers on Agriculture Department questionnaires would be available to local county tax assessors probably increased this tendency.

Chapter XVIII

Summary, Politics, and the Future

In this final chapter, please note the sequence of the words in the title. First, we will summarize the book which has dealt principally with the history of the livestock industry. Second, we will review the part government has and will play in this field. Third, we will discuss the future, which, fortunately or unfortunately, depending on your economic views, is largely going to be shaped by governmental action. As mentioned in the preface, various portions of this book were prepared separately during the period 1955 to 1960, which was a period of violent change and price fluctuation. Consequently, this accounts for various discrepancies in financial projections and other material.

We have covered the life cycle of a beef cow; its care, feed and management; the various methods and techniques of marketing; and the history and origin of the principal beef breeds. From the land standpoint, we have reviewed the various techniques of land management; the rise and fall of the large cattle kingdoms; and the historical techniques of absentee ownership where one man owned the cattle, another man owned the land, and a third man did the work. Finally, we covered the economic aspects of the industry; the projection of breeding herd growth and maintenance costs; the effects of the Federal tax laws and a review of recent cases; and the economic effect in recent years of farm and ranch consolidation as related to unit operational costs.

At this point, from a strictly operational point of view and not considering certain tax advantages, it does not take a financial wizard to see that the two or three percent that an investor can make out of breeding cattle or out of ranchland, does not justify the wildly fluctuating prices and the many hazards of weather, disease and poor management that he must risk.

First, we would like to dispel the fiction of the millionaire rancher who made it on operations. Outside of possibly the dozen in the United States who have consistently been able to "buy low and sell high," the rest are making their money from the following:

1. Their oil and mineral revenues.

2. Selling off portions of their ranch for suburban developments or to "city ranchers."
3. Having inherited enormous tracts of land from their grandfather who got it at fifty cents an acre, they forget to throw a normal return on the market value of their land into their operating costs for analysis purposes.
4. They neglect to consider their own managerial abilities or the wages of their sons at market value as part of their operating costs. Even our absentee investor can make a decent return if he wishes to give it the supreme effort.

To illustrate the problem, let us compare a small local farmer with an operator on a national scale using leased lands and hiring all services including top management: Using the Missouri area as an example, farmer John Doe, who has two teen-age sons, and operates an 800 acre cattle farm with no mortgage in an area of low real estate taxes and who is willing to start work at 5:00 in the morning, can maintain a cow-calf for a year at around $35.00. This includes about a 3% return on his farm land, but *nothing* for the labor of himself and his sons. He raises his own feed except for the little that he has been buying each year from his cousin who runs a farm down the road. With a considerable effort, John Doe and his sons manage to net about $4,000.00 per year for their own labor in managing the herd and raising feed after paying for new machinery and necessary maintenance on the farm.

Now what happens to the wealthy Tom Smith, a large multiple herd owner, who lives in New York? First, when he leases land the owner wants to net 6% instead of 3%. Second, he is operating herds all over the United States, doesn't have enough "cousins living down the road" and has to pay more for his feed. Third, he has to hire John Doe, but he doesn't get the two sons because they can now get $1.50 per hour working in the neighboring factory town. Fourth, John Doe, himself, now that he is working for somebody else, starts the day at 7:30 A.M. instead of 5:00 A.M. Fifth, extra labor on the farm now costs $200.00 per month plus board and is only half as efficient as John Doe's sons who would rather work in town. Sixth, Tom Smith has to hire Johnny Jones at $5.00 per head to supervise the half dozen John Doe deals that he has in this part of the state. Seventh, he has to pay a management firm about $4.00 per head to do his bookkeeping, negotiate his bank loans, and hire and inspect the Johnny Joneses all over the United States.

At any stage of the game, Tom Smith could move in and cut his operating costs. First, he could handle his own loans, his own bookkeeping, and his own inspecting and save $4.00 per head. Second, he could take up residence in Valentine, Nebraska; limit his operations to the Nebraska-South Dakota area; check each one of his half dozen ranches once a week; and save himself another $5.00 per head. Third, he can yank his two sons out of Harvard and Groton; move on to a farm; get up with his boys at 4:30 in the morning to start feeding at 5:00 A.M.; and he will be able to cut $25.00 more off his operating costs.

In some cases, Tom Smith, as a large national scale operator, will get certain advantages over John Doe, particularly as soon as his operation in a given geographic area has been in effect for a couple of years. First, he can use his mass purchasing power to get a better price. Second, by being able to pay cash in advance for pastures, he can make better deals with money-short landlords than can John Doe who pays so much per head per month if he rents land. Third, as soon as the local banks get used to him he will be able to borrow at a 2% better rate. Fourth, by being spread all over the United States, a single local disaster won't wipe him out as it will John Doe. In the same light, if a drought or crop failure occurs in a given area, he can always move to another geographic area where he is already established and operating and will only be out the cost of transporting the animals. Fifth, many of the extra cost items pointed out above disappear after he has been operating in a new area several years. For example, while Tom Smith has "no cousin living down the road" to rent a corn field from, several of his hired hands do.

Strictly from a return on capital standpoint, why then is the beef industry in the United States today in such a poor net profit position? The answer is extremely simple and it applies to hogs as well as cattle. Beef and pork are on a free market, but feed is artificially supported by the Federal Government.

Prior to the crop support program, in times of economic disaster when the livestock markets collapsed, grain and feed went down simultaneously, so the relatively competent operator was able to at least preserve the basic herd. Today in a distressed market, his raw materials are artificially kept high and he is caught in a squeeze.

This works indirectly as well as directly. For example, land that would ordinarily be too marginal to be cultivated and would be available for rent as pasture is put into wheat because of the high wheat supports with the grain eventually destined for Federal storage.

A further sidelight on this picture is the fact that duties and tariffs on the foreign imports of cattle are relatively low as compared with most other commodities and goods. Consequently, on the few occasions in recent years when cattle prices went high enough to compensate the ranchers for the many years they were losing money, in rolled foreign imports in sufficient volume to take the edge off. What, then, are these government agencies and programs that I consider to be so important as to be the major factors in the next few years for the future of the livestock industry?

1. The price support program of the Department of Agriculture, whether it is operating through the parity system and loans of the CCC, or whether it is operating under the acreage restriction system. "Parity" is a complicated formula supposedly reflecting the purchasing power of produce the farmer sells at the price level of a base period, 1909 to 1914, and is the basis for the amount of loan that a given crop will get in a given area. The loan is without recourse except for the grain and it is anticipated that normally the government will recapture the grain and put it in some form of Federally subsidized storage.

2. Both Democrats and Republicans are advocating a massive return to some combination of the old soil bank program or the later soil conservation program. This involved taking large acreages out of crop or hay production and putting them into a non-use status with the Federal Government paying higher than market rents while they remained in this status.

3. In the more arid sections of the West, the larger ranches are principally operating on leases on government grazing land. Future Federal policy on National Forest permits, modifications in the old Taylor Rights of the new Bureau of Land Management, Department of Interior action on Indian reservation leases, and Department of Defense policy on military reservation leases will be principal factors in the cow-herd portion of the livestock industry. As the various homestead laws caused a revolution in the Cattle Kingdoms of three generations ago, so the new practice of competitive sealed bids on public leased grazing lands is causing a major upheaval in the Big Spreads of today.

4. Income tax laws, and in particular inheritance taxes on the new highly inflated land values, are going to work in opposite directions. Federal tax subsidies on both land improvement and the accumulation and up-breeding of herds are encouraging new people with large capital to come into the industry. On the other hand, inheritance taxes are breaking up the vast land accumulations of the past.

5. The Cattle Lobbies are pushing for higher tariffs and duties on imports but the free trade advocates are fighting them.

6. Both political parties are exploring the possibility of converting surplus feed into livestock and exporting protein products as part of the Foreign Aid program so as not to upset the grain economies of many of our friends and allies. There is also talk of a massive program of shipping out actual top breeding stock under a government subsidy or with foreign aid credits so as to upgrade the economies of some of the new nations as well as a number of the Latin American countries.

For the next five years it is my opinion that the biggest influences on the U. S. cattle industry in a descending order of importance will be: first, governmental actions; second, consolidation of small farms and ranches into big ones; third, new technical developments.

INDEX